A READING GUIDE TO THE OLD TESTAMENT

DAVID H. MULHOLLAND

Deseret Book Company
Salt Lake City, Utah

My thanks to my wife, Lois,
to our children, David, John, Brian, Sarah, Roger, and Matthew,
for allowing me the time necessary to write,
and to others who have given me the benefit of their knowledge of
the Old Testament

©1989 David H. Mulholland

ISBN 0-87579-283-9

Printed in the United States of America
10   9   8   7   6   5   4   3   2   1

Contents

Preface iv

How to Use This Reading Guide 1

Questions about the Bible 3

Questions about the Old Testament 6

Questions about the Pearl of Great Price .227

Answers 237

Preface

This guide will help you better understand the Old Testament. As you focus on its principles and stories you will be motivated to draw closer to God by keeping his commandments.

"Some of the lessons and insights that make a careful study of the Old Testament not only meaningful but critical are—

"1. The testimony of the existence of God.

"2. The record of the beginnings of mankind as a divine race placed on the earth for eternal, divine purposes.

"3. The importance of establishing a covenant relationship with God.

"4. The history and purpose of the establishment of the elect lineage through which the priesthood would be restored and the blessings of the gospel extended to all in the last days.

"5. The revelation of a divine law upon which civil and criminal codes of many nations would be built.

"6. The knowledge that God intervenes directly in the lives of men and nations and that through him many are divinely led, directed, and protected.

"7. The blessings of obedience to the laws of God and faith in his name.

"8. The consequences of disobedience and rebellion against God and his laws.

"9. The corruption that results from any form of idolatry and the reasons for the commandments of the Lord against it.

"10. The need to live and endure throughout mortality in obedience to God's laws, even though suffering and pain and persecution may come.

"11. The way by which the Saints can escape the corruptions and resulting judgments of the last days.

"12. The promises of a literal gathering of Israel in the last days and a time of restoration and redemption for Israel.

"13. The greatness and dreadfulness of the day when the Lord will come in his glory.

"14. The testimony that the God of the Old Testament is Jesus Christ and that he came to earth to free men from death and make it possible for men to be freed from sin and thus return to the presence of God the Father." (Old Testament: 1 Kings–Malachi [Religion 301 student manual], Salt Lake City: The Church of Jesus Christ of Latter-day Saints, p. v.)

How to Use This Reading Guide

When you begin your study of the Old Testament, first read the headnote to the chapter you are studying and then read the chapter itself. Refer to the footnotes as you read. Both the headnotes and the footnotes will help you understand better what you read in the chapter. They will also help you answer the questions in this guide.

Next, go back through the chapter you have just read, review the headnote and the footnotes, and then write in the guide the answer to each question and the number of the verse or verses where each answer is found. You will find most of the answers in the chapter you are reading in the Old Testament, but you may need to look for a few answers in other places in the scriptures.

The designation "See" after a question refers you to the passage where you will find the answer. This designation is used only when the full answer is not in the chapter you are currently reading. For example, "See 2 Samuel 24:16*a*" after a question means that you will find all or part of the answer in footnote *a* to verse 16 of 2 Samuel 24.

The designation "See also" refers you to related information that is not necessarily part of the answer. For example, you may be referred to the Bible Dictionary, which is in the appendix to the Latter-day Saint edition of the King James Version of the Bible.

Compare the verse or verses you wrote down with the verses listed in the Answers section at the back of this book. The Answers section should be used as a guide; you may find some answers in other verses not listed there.

In addition to the scriptures and this guide, the Old Testament student manuals prepared by the Church Educational System will help you better understand the history and doctrine you are reading:

Old Testament: Genesis–2 Samuel (Salt Lake City: The Church of Jesus Christ of Latter-day Saints, 1981), and

Old Testament: 1 Kings–Malachi (Salt Lake City: The Church of Jesus Christ of Latter-day Saints, 1982).

An excellent source of in-depth information that will help you in your study of Isaiah is Avraham Gileadi's *The Book of Isaiah: A New Translation with Interpretive Keys from the Book of Mormon* (Salt Lake City: Deseret Book, 1988).

Questions about the Bible

Title Page

PAGE NUMBER

_____ a. What is the complete title of the Bible?

_____ b. How did the King James Version originate?

To the Most High and Mighty Prince James . . . : The Epistle Dedicatory

PAGE NUMBER

_____ a. What are the titles held by King James?

_____ b. Why did the translators pay King James this tribute?

The Names and Order of All the Books of the Old and New Testament

PAGE NUMBER

_____ a. How many books are in the Old Testament in the Latter-day Saint edition of the King James Version of the Bible?

_____ b. How many books are in the New Testament?

_____ c. List the five study aids in the Appendix.

Explanation Concerning Abbreviations

PAGE NUMBER

_____ a. Where are the listed abbreviations used?

_____ b. What does the abbreviation GR indicate?

_____ c. What does HC indicate?

_____ d. What does IE indicate?

_____ e. What does JST indicate? In what two places are the excerpts to be found?

_____ f. Where can you find the abbreviations for books of scripture contained in the Bible?

_____ g. Where can you find the abbreviations for books of scripture contained in the Book of Mormon, the Doctrine and Covenants, and the Pearl of Great Price?

Introduction to the Bible

See Bible Dictionary, page 622, s.v. "Bible."

_____ a. What is the Bible?

_____ b. What is meant by the word *bible?*

_____ c. Who originally wrote the various books in the Bible?

_____ d. What are the two great divisions of the Christian Bible?

_____ e. What language was most of the Old Testament originally written in?

_____ f. What does the word *testament* mean in Hebrew?

_____ g. What is the Old Covenant?

_____ h. What is the New Covenant?

_____ i. How does the arrangement of books in the Hebrew Bible differ from that in the Christian Bible?

_____ j. How many books does the Latter-day Saint edition of the King James Version of the Bible have?

_____ k. What did the scholars do who formed the Jewish school at Tiberias?

_____ l. What evidence do the Dead Sea Scrolls provide?

_____ m. What three kinds of evidence are used to determine the text of the New Testament?

_____ n. What is the position of The Church of Jesus Christ of Latter-day Saints regarding the Bible?

_____ o. What did Joseph Smith teach concerning the Bible?

_____ p. What has the Lord given us to sustain, support, and verify the Bible?

See Bible Dictionary, page 624, s.v. "Bible, English."

_____ a. To whom does the "honor of making the first translation of the Bible into English from the languages in which it was originally written" belong?

_____ b. What happened to him in 1536? Why?

_____ c. How many years were required to translate the "Authorized Version"?

See Bible Dictionary, page 717, s.v. "Joseph Smith Translation (JST)."

_____ a. What is the Joseph Smith Translation?

_____ b. When was most of Joseph Smith's translation of the Bible completed?

_____ c. What would Joseph Smith have done "had he lived to publish the entire work"?

_____ d. What did the Prophet receive as a direct consequence of making this translation?

_____ e. What does the Joseph Smith Translation to some extent assist in doing?

_____ f. Why is the Joseph Smith Translation important to students of the scriptures?

See Bible Dictionary, page 630, s.v. "Canon."

_____ a. What did _canon_ originally mean in Greek?

_____ b. What is _canon_ used to mean now?

_____ c. What do we learn from modern revelation about the preservation of the books of the Bible?

_____ d. How did the Gospels come into being?

_____ e. What was the primary purpose of the epistles?

_____ f. List three rules that were used to determine the validity of certain writings as scripture.

_____ g. When and how will additions be made to the current collection of scripture?

See Bible Dictionary, page 748, s.v. "Pentateuch."

_____ a. What does _pentateuch_ mean in Greek?

_____ b. To what books has the name Pentateuch been given?

_____ c. Who wrote the Pentateuch?

_____ d. What fundamental truths do we find in the Pentateuch?

_____ e. What is a major contribution of the Pentateuch?

Questions about the Old Testament

The First Book of Moses, Called GENESIS

Introduction

See Bible Dictionary, page 678, s.v. "Genesis."

_____ a. What does *genesis* mean?

_____ b. List seven "beginnings" that are recorded in the book of Genesis.

_____ c. List five major divisions in the book.

_____ d. What is the object of the book?

_____ e. List four religious ideas that Genesis contains.

_____ f. Why is Moses 1 of exceptional worth to the study of Genesis?

_____ g. List four sources of latter-day revelation that clarify Genesis.

Genesis 1

VERSE NUMBER

_____ a. What did God do on each day of the Creation? (See also Bible Dictionary, p. 681, s.v. "God.")

6

_____ Day 1

_____ Day 2

_____ Day 3

_____ Day 4

_____ Day 5

_____ Day 6

_____ Day 7 (See Genesis 2:1–3.)

Genesis 2

_____ a. What information in Moses 3:5 clarifies Genesis 2:5? (See Moses 3:5.)

_____ b. What trees did God put in the Garden?

_____ c. What did God say about "the tree of the knowledge of good and evil"? (Genesis 2:17.)

_____ d. Who and what did Adam give names to?

_____ e. Why was Adam's "help meet" called woman? (V. 18; see also 18*b*.)

Genesis 3

_____ a. How did Satan persuade Eve to eat the fruit?

_____ b. Why did Adam and Eve hide when they heard the Lord approaching?

_____ c. How was the serpent cursed?

_____ d. What happened to Eve because she ate of the fruit of the tree?

_____ e. What happened to Adam because he ate of the fruit of the tree?

_____ f. Why did Adam call his wife Eve? (See also Bible Dictionary, p. 668, s.v. "Eve.")

_____ g. Why were Adam and Eve sent out of the Garden? (See also 2 Nephi 2:22–26; Bible Dictionary, p. 670, s.v. "Fall of Adam.")

Genesis 4

_____ a. What did Cain offer to the Lord? (See also Moses 5:19; Bible Dictionary, p. 628, s.v. "Cain.")

_____ b. What did Abel offer to the Lord? (See also Moses 5:5–7; Bible Dictionary, p. 600 s.v. "Abel.")

_____ c. How did Cain respond when the Lord did not accept his offering?

_____ d. What did Cain say when the Lord asked about Abel?

_____ e. How was Cain punished for killing Abel?

_____ f. What did Eve say of Seth?

Genesis 5

_____ a. What name did God give to Adam and Eve when they were created? (See also Genesis 5:2a.)

_____ b. Who was the son of Enoch?

_____ c. What happened to Enoch? (See also v. 24a; Bible Dictionary, p. 665, s.v. "Enoch.")

_____ d. What is the name of the son of Methuselah?

_____ e. How old was Methuselah when he died?

_____ f. Who was Noah's father?

_____ g. What do we know about Noah's three sons? (See Bible Dictionary, p. 698, s.v. "Ham"; p. 710, s.v. "Japheth"; p. 773, s.v. "Shem.")

Genesis 6

_____ a. What thoughts did men continually have?

_____ b. How did the Lord feel toward the wickedness on the earth? (See also Genesis 6:6a.)

_____ c. What was the condition of the earth before the Flood?

_____ d. What was Noah instructed to do? (See also Bible Dictionary, p. 613, s.v. "Ark.")

_____ e. What did the Lord covenant with Noah to do?

_____ f. What things did Noah do?

Genesis 7

_____ a. Why did the Lord instruct Noah to get himself and all of his family into the ark?

_____ b. Why did the Lord instruct Noah to take the beasts and the fowls of the air?

_____ c. How long was it to rain?

_____ d. Which people were saved in the ark?

_____ e. What was destroyed by the Flood?

_____ f. How long did the waters last on the earth?

Genesis 8

_____ a. How did Noah know when the earth was dry?

_____ b. How did Noah know when to leave the ark?

_____ c. What did Noah build "unto the Lord"? (Genesis 8:20.)

_____ d. What did Noah say in his heart? (See JST Genesis 9:4–6.)

Genesis 9

_____ a. What did the Lord say to Noah and his sons in verse 1? (See also Genesis 9:1c.)

_____ b. What was given to Noah and his family for food?

_____ c. What were they not to eat? (See JST Genesis 9:10.)

_____ d. When should we kill animals? (See JST Genesis 9:11.)

_____ e. What is to happen to people who kill others? (See JST Genesis 9:12–13.)

_____ f. What covenant did God make with Noah? (See also Bible Dictionary, p. 651, s.v. "Covenant.")

_____ g. What covenant did the Lord make with Enoch? (See Genesis 9:9a; JST Genesis 9:21–23.)

_____ h. What is the token of this covenant? (See also JST Genesis 9:24–25.)

_____ i. Who was the father of Canaan?

_____ j. How was Canaan cursed? (See also Moses 7:7–12; Abraham 1:21–27.)

Genesis 10

_____ a. Who was the "mighty hunter before the Lord"? (Genesis 10:9.)

_____ b. In whose days was the earth divided? (See also D&C 133:23–24.)

_____ c. How were the nations divided on the earth after the Flood?

Genesis 11

VERSE NUMBER

_____ a. Who inspired the people to build the tower? (See Helaman 6:28.)

_____ b. Why did the Lord confound their language?

_____ c. Why was the tower called Babel?

_____ d. Which of Noah's three sons was Abram (later Abraham) descended from?

Genesis 12

VERSE NUMBER

_____ a. List four things the Lord told Abram before he left Haran.

_____ b. Why did Abram go to Egypt? (See also Map 2, yellow arrow; Bible Dictionary, p. 660, s.v. "Egypt.")

_____ c. What did the Lord say to Abram when he went into Egypt? (See Abraham 2:22–24.)

_____ d. How were Abram and Sarai accepted in Egypt?

_____ e. Why did the Lord send great plagues to Pharaoh and his house?

_____ f. What did Pharaoh do?

Genesis 13

VERSE NUMBER

_____ a. Why were Abram and Lot unable to dwell together?

_____ b. How did Abram solve the problem?

_____ c. Where did Lot go to live? Why?

_____ d. Why did God judge the men of Sodom to be wicked? (See Genesis 13:13b.)

_____ e. What did the Lord say to Abram after Lot had left? (See also v. 14a.)

_____ f. Where did Abram settle? (See also Bible Dictionary, p. 699, s.v. "Hebron"; Map 1.)

Genesis 14

VERSE NUMBER

_____ a. Who and what did the kings take from Sodom and Gomorrah?

_____ b. Who and what did Abram bring back?

_____ c. What did Melchizedek, king of Salem, do when Abram returned? (See Genesis 14:18d; see also Bible Dictionary, p. 730, s.v. "Melchizedek" and "Melchizedek Priesthood.")

_____ d. To whom did Abram pay his tithing? (See also JST Genesis 14:39–40; Alma 13:15; see also Bible Dictionary, p. 785, s.v. "Tithe.")

_____ e. Why did Abram refuse to accept the goods offered by the king of Sodom?

_____ f. What oath did God make with Enoch concerning the priesthood? (See JST Genesis 14:30–31.)

Genesis 15

VERSE NUMBER

_____ a. What did Abram desire from the Lord?

_____ b. What did the Lord show Abram? (See JST Genesis 15:12.)

_____ c. What did Abram learn about his descendants? (See Genesis 15:13a.)

Genesis 16

VERSE NUMBER

_____ a. Why did Sarai give Hagar to Abram? (See D&C 132:34–35.)

_____ b. Why was Sarai despised by Hagar?

_____ c. What did Sarai say to Abram? (See also D&C 64:9–11.)

_____ d. Why did Hagar leave?

_____ e. What did the angel of the Lord say to Hagar?

_____ f. What does the name Ishmael mean? (See Genesis 16:11a; see also Bible Dictionary, p. 707, s.v. "Ishmael.")

Genesis 17

VERSE NUMBER

_____ a. Why was Abram's name changed to Abraham?

_____ b. What two things did the Lord covenant to do for Abraham and his seed?

_____ c. What was to be the sign of the covenant? (See also Genesis 17:13a; JST Genesis 17:11–12.)

_____ d. What does the name Sarah mean? (See Genesis 17:15a.)

_____ e. How was Sarah to be blessed?

_____ f. How did Abraham respond to Sarah's blessing? (See v. 17a.)

_____ g. With whom would God establish his covenant? (See also Bible Dictionary, p. 707, s.v. "Isaac.")

_____ h. When were Abraham and all the males of his house circumcised? (See also Bible Dictionary, p. 646, s.v. "Circumcision.")

Genesis 18

VERSE NUMBER

_____ a. What did Abraham say to the three men? (See also Genesis 18:3a.)

_____ b. What message did they deliver to Abraham and Sarah?

_____ c. What kind of man did the Lord know Abraham to be?

_____ d. Who were the angels who visited Abraham? (See v. 22a.)

_____ e. How many righteous people were to be found to save Sodom from destruction?

Genesis 19

VERSE NUMBER

_____ a. How many angels went to Sodom? (See Genesis 19:1a.)

_____ b. What did Lot do for them?

_____ c. Why did the men of Sodom go to Lot's house? (See v. 5a.)

_____ d. What did Lot say about his two daughters? (See JST Genesis 19:13.)

_____ e. Why were the men unable to break down Lot's door?

_____ f. Why had the Lord sent the three angels to Sodom?

_____ g. How was Lot's warning to leave received by his sons-in-law?

_____ h. How were Sodom and Gomorrah destroyed?

_____ i. Why did Lot's wife become a pillar of salt?

_____ j. What wicked thing did Lot and his daughters do? How did Lot's daughters justify themselves? (See Genesis 19:35a.)

Genesis 20

_____ a. What did Abraham say of Sarah?

_____ b. Why did God not destroy Abimelech?

_____ c. How was Sarah Abraham's sister?

_____ d. How did God punish the house of Abimelech? Why?

Genesis 21

_____ a. What did Abraham do when Isaac was eight days old?

_____ b. Why did Sarah ask Abraham to cast out Hagar and Ishmael?

_____ c. How was Abraham comforted?

_____ d. What did Abraham do early in the morning?

_____ e. How were Hagar and Ishmael saved in the wilderness? Why?

_____ f. From what land did Hagar obtain a wife for Ishmael?

_____ g. What covenant did Abraham make with Abimelech?

_____ h. Why did Abraham give Abimelech seven ewe lambs?

Genesis 22

_____ a. Why did the Lord visit Abraham? (See Genesis 22:1a.)

_____ b. What did the Lord require of Abraham?

_____ c. What did Abraham do "early in the morning"? (V. 3.)

_____ d. What happened as Abraham was about to kill Isaac? (See also Bible Dictionary, p. 608, s.v. "Angels.")

_____ e. How was Abraham blessed? Why?

Genesis 23

_____ a. What did Abraham desire of the sons of Heth?

_____ b. What was their reply?

_____ c. How was the ownership of the field and cave "made sure unto Abraham"? (Genesis 23:20.)

Genesis 24

_____ a. What oath did the servant swear to Abraham?

_____ b. What did the servant request of God?

_____ c. What happened before the servant had finished speaking?

_____ d. How was Rebekah's grandfather related to Abraham? (See Abraham 2:2.)

_____ e. What did Laban do for Abraham's servants?

_____ f. What did Laban and Bethuel say to the servant?

_____ g. What did Rebekah's family say to her before she left?

_____ h. How did Isaac feel toward Rebekah?

Genesis 25

_____ a. To whom did Abraham give all that he had?

_____ b. What did Abraham give to his other sons?

_____ c. How old was Abraham when he died?

_____ d. Who buried Abraham?

_____ e. Why did the children struggle in Rebekah's womb? (See also Bible Dictionary, p. 667, s.v. "Esau"; p. 708, s.v. "Jacob.")

_____ f. Why did Isaac love Esau?

_____ g. Why did Esau sell his birthright to Isaac for the pottage? (See also Bible Dictionary, p. 625, s.v. "Birthright.")

Genesis 26

VERSE NUMBER

_____ a. What did the Lord say to Isaac?

_____ b. Why did Isaac say Rebekah was his sister?

_____ c. What did Abimelech tell his people about Isaac and Rebekah?

_____ d. How did Isaac become great?

_____ e. What did Abimelech say to Isaac? Why?

_____ f. What did Isaac do?

_____ g. Why did Abimelech visit Isaac?

Genesis 27

VERSE NUMBER

_____ a. What did Isaac request of Esau?

_____ b. What did Rebekah say to Jacob?

_____ c. What blessing did Jacob receive from Isaac? (See also Genesis 25:29–34.)

_____ d. What does the name Jacob mean? (See Genesis 27:36a.)

_____ e. What blessing did Esau receive from Isaac?

_____ f. How did Esau feel toward Jacob?

_____ g. Where did Rebekah send Jacob?

Genesis 28

VERSE NUMBER

_____ a. What charge and blessing were given to Jacob by Isaac?

_____ b. Where did Isaac send Jacob?

_____ c. What did the Lord tell Jacob in his dream?

_____ d. What vow did Jacob make to the Lord?

Genesis 29

_____ a. Whom did Jacob meet at the well?

_____ b. How was Jacob received by Laban?

_____ c. What did Jacob ask of Laban for wages?

_____ d. Why did Laban give Leah to Jacob?

_____ e. How many years did Jacob work for Rachel?

_____ f. What did the Lord do for Leah? Why?

Genesis 30

_____ a. Why did Rachel envy Leah?

_____ b. Whom did Rachel give to Jacob? Why? (See also Genesis 30:3a.)

_____ c. What are mandrakes? (See Bible Dictionary, p. 728, s.v. "Mandrakes.")

_____ d. Who was the first son of Rachel?

_____ e. Why did Laban want Jacob to stay?

_____ f. What agreement did Jacob and Laman make?

_____ g. How did Jacob increase his flocks?

Genesis 31

_____ a. What did the Lord instruct Jacob to do? (See also Bible Dictionary, p. 708, s.v. "Jacob.")

_____ b. How had God blessed Jacob for his loyalty to Laban?

_____ c. What did Leah and Rachel say to Jacob?

_____ d. What had Rachel stolen?

_____ e. What did Laban say to Jacob when they met?

_____ f. What covenant did Jacob and Laban make with each other?

Genesis 32

_____ a. Who met Jacob when he returned home?

_____ b. What message did Jacob send to Esau?

_____ c. What did Jacob do because he was "greatly afraid"? (Genesis 32:7.)

_____ d. Why did Jacob send his gifts as he did?

_____ e. Why was Jacob's name changed to Israel? (See also v. 28b.)

_____ f. Why did Jacob call the name of the place Peniel? (See also v. 30a.)

Genesis 33

_____ a. How did Esau greet Jacob?

_____ b. Why did Jacob want Esau to keep his gifts?

_____ c. Why did Jacob choose not to go with Esau to Sier?

_____ d. What did Jacob do in Succoth?

Genesis 34

_____ a. What did Shechem do when he saw Dinah?

_____ b. Upon what condition did the sons of Jacob consent to giving Dinah to Shechem? (See also Genesis 34:14a.)

_____ c. What did Simeon and Levi do?

_____ d. What was Jacob's response to their actions?

Genesis 35

_____ a. What did God tell Jacob to do?

_____ b. What did Jacob say to all his household?

_____ c. Why did the neighboring cities not pursue Jacob?

_____ d. What did God say to Jacob?

_____ e. What happened to Rachel when Benjamin was born?

_____ f. Who buried Isaac?

Genesis 36

_____ a. Whose descendants are listed in Genesis 36?

Genesis 37

_____ a. What did Israel make for Joseph? (See also Genesis 37:3c.)

_____ b. Why did Joseph's brethren hate him?

_____ c. What did Joseph see in his two dreams?

_____ d. Who counseled his brothers not to kill Joseph?

_____ e. How was Joseph taken to Egypt?

_____ f. What did Joseph's brothers tell Jacob?

_____ g. Who was Potiphar? (See also v. 36c, d.)

Genesis 38

_____ a. Why did the Lord slay Er, Judah's firstborn?

_____ b. Why did Tamar play the harlot?

Genesis 39

_____ a. What did Potiphar notice about Joseph?

_____ b. Why did the Lord bless Potiphar?

_____ c. What kind of person was Joseph?

_____ d. How persistent was Potiphar's wife?

_____ e. What did Joseph do?

_____ f. What did she tell Potiphar when he returned?

_____ g. How did the Lord bless Joseph in prison?

Genesis 40

_____ a. Why were Pharaoh's butler and baker in prison?

_____ b. What was the interpretation of the butler's dream?

_____ c. What did Joseph ask of the butler after interpreting his dream?

_____ d. What was the interpretation of the baker's dream?

Genesis 41

_____ a. What did Pharaoh dream?

_____ b. Whom did Pharaoh call to interpret his dreams?

_____ c. Why did Pharaoh call for Joseph?

_____ d. Whom did Joseph say would provide the interpretation?

_____ e. What was the interpretation of Pharaoh's dream?

_____ f. What did Joseph counsel Pharaoh to do?

_____ g. Why did Pharaoh appoint Joseph to be over his house?

_____ h. How much power did Joseph have?

_____ i. What were the names of Joseph's two sons?

_____ j. How far did the famine spread?

Genesis 42

_____ a. Why did Jacob send his sons to Egypt?

_____ b. Why did Benjamin not go to Egypt?

_____ c. What did Joseph do so his brothers would not recognize him?

_____ d. What did Joseph require of his brothers to prove themselves?

_____ e. Why were Joseph's brothers afraid?

_____ f. Why did Jacob want Benjamin not to go to Egypt?

Genesis 43

_____ a. Upon what condition would Jacob's sons return to Egypt?

_____ b. What did Jacob instruct his sons to take with them?

_____ c. Where did Joseph have his brothers taken when they returned?

_____ d. Why did Joseph go to his chamber?

_____ e. Why did Joseph refrain from eating bread with his brothers?

Genesis 44

_____ a. What did Joseph command the steward to put in the food sacks?

_____ b. Why were Joseph's brothers taken back to him?

_____ c. What did Judah say to Joseph?

Genesis 45

_____ a. How did Joseph make himself known to his brothers?

_____ b. Why were his brothers unable to answer him?

_____ c. How did Joseph comfort his brothers?

_____ d. What did Joseph instruct his brothers to say to Jacob?

_____ e. How was the arrival of Joseph's brothers received by Pharaoh?

_____ f. What did Pharaoh instruct Joseph to do?

_____ g. How did Jacob receive the news that Joseph was alive?

Genesis 46

_____ a. How did Jacob learn the will of the Lord concerning his move to Egypt?

_____ b. How many people of Jacob's house came to Egypt? (See also Exodus 1:5.)

_____ c. How did Joseph receive his father?

_____ d. How did Joseph plan to keep his family separated from the Egyptians?

Genesis 47

_____ a. What did Joseph's brothers say to Pharaoh?

_____ b. What did Pharaoh say to Joseph?

_____ c. What did Jacob do for Pharaoh?

_____ d. Where did Joseph settle his family?

_____ e. What did Joseph buy for Pharaoh?

_____ f. How much of Egyptians' increase was to be given to Pharaoh?

_____ g. What did Joseph promise Jacob he would do?

Genesis 48

_____ a. What blessing did Jacob give Ephraim and Manasseh? (See JST Genesis 48:5–6.)

_____ b. What blessing did Jacob give to Joseph? (See JST Genesis 48:7–11.)

_____ c. What did Jacob say to Joseph before he died?

Genesis 49

_____ a. Whom did Jacob bless before his death?

_____ b. How long was Judah to bear rule of the twelve tribes?

_____ c. Who were Joseph's branches that would "run over the wall"? (V. 22.)

_____ d. How will Christ bless Joseph?

Genesis 50

_____ a. How long did it take to embalm Jacob?

_____ b. What did Joseph ask of Pharaoh?

_____ c. Who went with Joseph to bury Jacob?

_____ d. What did Joseph say to his brothers about being sold into Egypt?

_____ e. What did Joseph prophesy about Moses? (See JST Genesis 50:24, 29, 34–35.)

_____ f. What did Joseph prophesy about Joseph Smith? (See JST Genesis 50:25–30, 32–33; see also 2 Nephi 3:4–15.)

_____ g. What did Joseph prophesy about the Bible and Book of Mormon? (See JST Genesis 50:31; see also Ezekiel 37:16–17; 2 Nephi 29.)

_____ h. What did the children of Israel do with Joseph's body after he died? (See JST Genesis 50:38.)

The Second Book of Moses, Called EXODUS

Introduction

Bible Dictionary, page 668, s.v. "Exodus."

_____ a. What does *exodus* mean?

_____ b. Why is this book called the book of Exodus?

_____ c. What are the two main divisions in the book?

_____ d. List ten things we learn in the first division.

_____ e. List six things we learn in the second division.

_____ f. What are the three stages of the early history of Israel described in Exodus?

Exodus 1

VERSE NUMBER

_____ a. How did the Lord bless the descendants of Jacob?

_____ b. Why did the Egyptians afflict them?

_____ c. Why did the midwives choose to disobey Pharaoh?

_____ d. What did Pharaoh charge his people to do with the Israelite babies?

Exodus 2

VERSE NUMBER

_____ a. What did the mother of Moses do when he was three months old?

_____ b. Who discovered the ark?

_____ c. What did Moses do when he was discovered in the ark?

_____ d. Who nursed the child?

_____ e. Why did Moses kill the Egyptian?

_____ f. Why did Moses flee from Pharaoh?

_____ g. How did Moses help the daughters of the priest of Midian?

_____ h. Why did the children of Israel cry to God?

Exodus 3

_____ a. Who appeared to Moses in a flame of fire? (See Exodus 3:2*a*.)

_____ b. What did the Lord call Moses to do?

_____ c. What did the Lord tell Moses to do?

_____ d. What would the Lord do in Egypt before his people would be let go?

_____ e. How would the Lord give his people "favour in the sight of the Egyptians"? (V. 21.)

Exodus 4

_____ a. What three signs did the Lord provide Moses? Why?

_____ b. How did Moses feel about his calling? Why?

_____ c. Who was appointed to be a spokesman for Moses? (See also Exodus 4:16*b*.)

_____ d. Whom did Moses take with him to Egypt?

_____ e. What would Pharaoh do when he saw the signs? (See v. 21*c*.)

_____ f. What was Moses to say to Pharaoh?

_____ g. Why was the Lord about to kill Moses? (See JST Exodus 4:24.)

_____ h. Whom did Moses and Aaron gather?

_____ i. What did Aaron say and do?

_____ j. How did the people respond to the Lord's message?

Exodus 5

_____ a. What did Moses and Aaron say to Pharaoh?

_____ b. What was Pharaoh's reply?

_____ c. How did Pharaoh increase the burden on the people?

_____ d. What did Moses say to the Lord?

Exodus 6

_____ a. What did the Lord say to Moses?

_____ b. Who is Jehovah? (See Exodus 6:3c.)

_____ c. What did Moses say to the children of Israel?

_____ d. How was his message received? Why?

_____ e. What did Moses say to the Lord when he was asked to return to Pharaoh? (See v. 30a.)

Exodus 7

_____ a. What offices were Moses and Aaron appointed to by the Lord? (See Exodus 7:1b, c.)

_____ b. What would Pharaoh do when the Lord's message was delivered? (See v. 3a.)

_____ c. When would the Egyptians know that the Lord is the God of the children of Israel?

_____ d. How old was Moses when he spoke to Pharaoh?

_____ e. What miracle was performed to show the Lord's power?

_____ f. How did Pharaoh respond? (See v. 13a.)

_____ g. What was the first plague?

_____ h. What did the magicians do?

Exodus 8

_____ a. What was the second plague?

_____ b. What did the magicians do?

_____ c. How did Pharaoh respond?

_____ d. What did Pharaoh do after the plague of frogs?

_____ e. What was the third plague?

_____ f. What did the magicians try to do?

_____ g. What did the magicians say to Pharaoh?

_____ h. What was the fourth plague?

_____ i. How did Pharaoh respond?

Exodus 9

_____ a. What was the fifth plague?

_____ b. How did Pharaoh respond?

_____ c. What was the sixth plague?

_____ d. Why were the magicians unable to stand before Moses?

_____ e. How did Pharaoh respond? (See Exodus 9:12a.)

_____ f. What was the seventh plague?

_____ g. How did Pharaoh respond?

Exodus 10

_____ a. What was the eighth plague?

_____ b. How did Pharaoh respond? (See Exodus 10:20a.)

_____ c. What was the ninth plague?

_____ d. How did Pharaoh respond? (See v. 27a.)

Exodus 11

_____ a. What were the children of Israel to borrow from the Egyptians?

_____ b. What was the tenth plague?

_____ c. What would be the response of the Egyptians?

Exodus 12

_____ a. What were the children of Israel to do?

_____ b. What did the lamb without blemish represent? (See Exodus 12:5a.)

_____ c. What was this event to be called?

_____ d. What would the Lord do?

_____ e. Why should the people observe the feast of the unleavened bread?

_____ f. What were the people to say to their children when asked about the Passover?

_____ g. What did the Lord do that night?

_____ h. How did Pharaoh respond?

_____ i. About how many Israelite men left Egypt?

_____ j. Why did the people eat unleavened cakes?

_____ k. How long had the children of Israel stayed in Egypt?

Exodus 13

_____ a. Who were to be sanctified unto the Lord?

_____ b. What were the people to do each year for a week? Why?

_____ c. What were the people to tell their sons about redeeming the firstborn?

_____ d. Why did the Lord lead the people around the land of the Philistines instead of through it?

_____ e. Whose bones did Moses take out of Egypt? Why?

_____ f. How did the Lord lead his people?

Exodus 14

_____ a. Why did Pharaoh follow the Israelites? (See also Exodus 14:4a.)

_____ b. What did the Israelites do when they saw the Egyptians coming?

_____ c. What did Moses say to the people?

_____ d. What happened to "the pillar of the cloud"? (V. 19b; see also v. 20a.)

_____ e. What did the Lord cause the Red Sea to do?

_____ f. What did the children of Israel do?

_____ g. What did the Lord do to the Egyptians?

_____ h. What caused the people to fear and to believe the Lord and Moses?

Exodus 15

VERSE NUMBER

_____ a. Why did the children of Israel praise the Lord?

_____ b. Why did the people murmur against Moses?

_____ c. How did the Lord provide water?

_____ d. What was required of the people to avoid the diseases that came upon the Egyptians?

Exodus 16

VERSE NUMBER

_____ a. Why did the people murmur against Moses and Aaron?

_____ b. How did the Lord provide bread? Why?

_____ c. How did the Lord provide meat?

_____ d. Why was Moses "wroth with them"? (Exodus 16:20.)

_____ e. What did the people do on the sixth and seventh day? Why?

_____ f. How long did the people eat manna from the Lord?

Exodus 17

VERSE NUMBER

_____ a. Why did the people complain to Moses? (See also Exodus 17:2a.)

_____ b. How did the Lord provide water for the people?

_____ c. Why did Aaron and Hur hold up the hands of Moses?

Exodus 18

_____ a. Who was Jethro? (See also Exodus 4:18.)

_____ b. Who was Zipporah?

_____ c. What did Jethro do when he heard that God had brought Israel out of Egypt?

_____ d. How did Moses receive Jethro?

_____ e. What advice did Jethro give Moses? Why?

_____ f. What kind of men were to be appointed to judge the people?

Exodus 19

_____ a. Where did the Israelites camp? (See also Map 3.)

_____ b. What did the Lord instruct Moses to say to the people?

_____ c. Why did the Lord come to Moses in a thick cloud?

_____ d. What was to happen on the third day?

_____ e. What were the people to refrain from doing?

_____ f. Why did Moses go up to the top of Mount Sinai?

_____ g. Why did the Lord send Moses down the mount?

Exodus 20

_____ a. List the Ten Commandments.

_____ b. What did the people see and do?

_____ c. Why did the Lord visit the people? (See also Exodus 20:20e.)

_____ d. How were the people to make their altars?

Exodus 21

VERSE NUMBER

_____ a. What three things must a man do if he took another wife?

_____ b. What was the penalty for killing someone?

_____ c. What offenses were punishable by death?

Exodus 22

VERSE NUMBER

_____ a. What was required of him who stole and killed an ox or sheep?

_____ b. Who should not be suffered to live? (See Exodus 22:18a.)

_____ c. What was to happen to those who sacrificed to another god?

_____ d. What was to happen to those who mistreated the widows or the fatherless?

Exodus 23

VERSE NUMBER

_____ a. How were the Israelites to act regarding justice? (See also Exodus 23:2a, 3a, 8a.)

_____ b. What were the Israelites to do in the seventh year?

_____ c. List the three annual feasts the Israelites were to observe.

_____ d. How would the Lord lead his people to the place he had prepared for them?

_____ e. List four ways the Lord would bless Israel if they served him.

_____ f. How would the Lord drive other nations from their land?

_____ g. Why were other nations not to dwell with Israel?

Exodus 24

_____ a. How did the people respond when Moses delivered the Lord's message?

_____ b. Who saw the God of Israel?

_____ c. Why was Moses to go up to the mount?

_____ d. How many days was Moses in the mount? (See also Deuteronomy 9:11.)

Exodus 25

_____ a. What offering was Moses to accept from the people?

_____ b. What were the things offered to be used for? Why? (See also Bible Dictionary, p. 778, s.v. "Tabernacle.")

_____ c. Where was the Lord to meet with Moses? Why?

_____ d. What is a cubit? (See Bible Dictionary, p. 651, s.v. "Cubit.")

Exodus 26

_____ a. What was to be built with curtains and boards?

_____ b. What was the vail to separate?

_____ c. Where was the ark of testimony to be put?

Exodus 27

_____ a. What was to be in the tabernacle?

_____ b. Where was the light to always burn?

Exodus 28

_____ a. What were Aaron and his sons to do?

_____ b. What were Aaron's garments to include?

_____ c. What was the breastplate of judgment to contain?

_____ d. What do the terms *Urim* and *Thummim* mean in Hebrew? (See Exodus 28:30*a*.)

_____ e. What is the purpose of the Urim and Thummim? (See Bible Dictionary, p. 786, s.v. "Urim and Thummim.")

Exodus 29

_____ a. What was to happen to Aaron and his sons?

_____ b. What was made to remove the sins from the people?

_____ c. What promise did the Lord make?

Exodus 30

_____ a. What was to be placed before the vail?

_____ b. What was atonement to be made with?

_____ c. Why was the atonement money to be paid?

_____ d. What were the priests to use?

Exodus 31

_____ a. What were Bezaleel and Aholiab called to do?

_____ b. Why were the children of Israel to keep the Lord's Sabbaths?

_____ c. What was the penalty for disobeying the law of the Sabbath?

_____ d. What did the Lord give Moses on Mount Sinai when He finished talking with him?

Exodus 32

_____ a. Why did the people ask Aaron to make gods for them?

_____ b. What did Aaron make with the gold?

_____ c. How had the people "corrupted themselves"? (Exodus 32:7.)

_____ d. What did Moses say to the Lord to prevent the destruction of the people? (See v. 12b.)

_____ e. What did the Lord reply? (See JST Exodus 32:14.)

_____ f. What did Moses do with the tablets when he saw the people? Why?

_____ g. What did Moses do with the calf?

_____ h. Who gathered themselves on the Lord's side?

_____ i. Whom will the Lord blot out of his book?

_____ j. What did the Lord do to the people because they had made the calf?

Exodus 33

VERSE NUMBER

_____ a. Why did the Lord not go before the people?

_____ b. Why did the people go to the tabernacle?

_____ c. What did the people see as Moses entered the tabernacle?

_____ d. How did the Lord speak with Moses?

_____ e. How were the children of Israel to be separated from all other nations?

_____ f. Who will not see the Lord's face and live? (See JST Exodus 33:20.)

Exodus 34

VERSE NUMBER

_____ a. What did the Lord ask Moses to do?

_____ b. What law would the Lord give to the people? Why? (See JST Exodus 34:1–2; see also Bible Dictionary, p. 722, s.v. "Law of Moses.")

_____ c. What did Moses request of the Lord?

_____ d. What did the Lord tell Moses to be careful of?

_____ e. How long did Moses fast when he received the Ten Commandments? (See also Bible Dictionary, p. 671, s.v. "Fasts.")

_____ f. Why were Aaron and the children of Israel afraid to approach Moses?

_____ g. What did Moses do to calm their fears?

Exodus 35

VERSE NUMBER

_____ a. What did Moses say about the Sabbath day?

_____ b. Who was to bring gifts for the tabernacle?

_____ c. Who returned to Moses with their gifts?

_____ d. Which women spun with their hands?

_____ e. How had the Lord prepared Bezaleel and Aholiab to build the tabernacle?

Exodus 36

VERSE NUMBER

_____ a. Who came to do the work?

_____ b. Why did Moses command the people to stop bringing their gifts?

Exodus 37

VERSE NUMBER

_____ a. List nine items that Bezaleel made.

Exodus 38

VERSE NUMBER

_____ a. How many men made an offering unto the Lord?

Exodus 39

VERSE NUMBER

_____ a. What did Moses do when the tabernacle was finished?

Exodus 40

VERSE NUMBER

_____ a. What were Aaron and his sons given?

_____ b. What happened when "Moses finished the work"? (V. 33.)

_____ c. Why was Moses unable to enter the tent of the congregation?

_____ d. How did the children of Israel know when to journey?

_____ e. What was upon the tabernacle by day and by night "throughout all their journeys"? (V. 38.)

The Third Book of Moses, Called LEVITICUS

Introduction

Bible Dictionary, page 724, s.v. "Leviticus."

_____ a. List the five main parts of the book of Leviticus.

_____ b. What is the dominant theme of this book?

_____ c. What is the object of this book?

_____ d. What did the sacrifices represent?

_____ e. What did the consecration of the priesthood teach?

_____ f. What did the law of clean and unclean represent?

See Bible Dictionary, page 765, s.v. "Sacrifices."

_____ g. What was the sacrifice of the firstlings of the flock in similitude of?

_____ h. During what periods of the earth's history were sacrifices offered?

_____ i. What has replaced the "shedding of blood as a gospel ordinance"?

_____ j. What accompanied the sacrifices?

_____ k. What did the sacrifices represent?

_____ l. What were the three kinds of altar sacrifices under the Mosaic law?

_____ m. List the six important acts of animal sacrifices.

_____ n. What was the purpose of the sin, or trespass, offering?

_____ o. What was the purpose of the burnt offering?

_____ p. What was the purpose of the peace offering?

_____ q. What did these symbolic sacrifices represent when offered together?

Leviticus 1

VERSE NUMBER

_____ a. To whom did the Lord reveal the details of acceptable burnt offerings?

_____ b. Which of the three kinds of offerings is described?

_____ c. Why were "sacrifices of animals without blemish" made? (Headnote to Leviticus 1.)

_____ d. Who was to perform the sacrificial rites?

Leviticus 2

VERSE NUMBER

_____ a. What is described in Leviticus 2?

_____ b. What ingredients did the meat offering consist of?

_____ c. What portion of the meat offering was "a thing most holy of the offerings of the Lord made by fire"? (Leviticus 2:3.)

_____ d. What ingredients were prohibited?

Leviticus 3

VERSE NUMBER

_____ a. How were peace offerings made?

_____ b. What was Israel forbidden to eat?

Leviticus 4

VERSE NUMBER

_____ a. What kind of sin did this offering atone for?

_____ b. How were sinners forgiven?

_____ c. What did the priests do through the sin offering?

Leviticus 5

_____ a. What were the people to do regarding their sins?

_____ b. How did they obtain forgiveness?

Leviticus 6

_____ a. How were the people to obtain forgiveness for their sins?

_____ b. What was the regulation concerning the fire on the altar?

_____ c. Which two offerings could not be eaten?

Leviticus 7

_____ a. What laws are set forth in Leviticus 7?

_____ b. How was Israel to worship?

_____ c. List five things Israel was to do through sacrifice.

Leviticus 8

_____ a. What happened to Aaron and his sons?

_____ b. What did Moses and Aaron do?

Leviticus 9

_____ a. What did Aaron do?

_____ b. What appeared to all the people?

_____ c. What consumed the offerings on the altar?

Leviticus 10

VERSE NUMBER

_____ a. Who were Nadab and Abihu?

_____ b. What happened to them? Why?

Leviticus 11

VERSE NUMBER

_____ a. What did the Lord reveal to Moses and Aaron? (See also Bible Dictionary, p. 646, s.v. "Clean and Unclean.")

_____ b. What did the Lord command Israel to be?

Leviticus 12

VERSE NUMBER

_____ a. What law did the Lord reveal in Leviticus 12?

_____ b. How many days was the purification process for women who bore a male child? a female child?

Leviticus 13

VERSE NUMBER

_____ a. What laws and tokens were revealed in Leviticus 13?

_____ b. What happened to a leper "in whom the plague [was]"? (Leviticus 13:45.)

Leviticus 14

VERSE NUMBER

_____ a. What laws, rites, and sacrifices were revealed in Leviticus 14?

Leviticus 15

VERSE NUMBER

_____ a. What laws, rites, and sacrifices were revealed in Leviticus 15?

Leviticus 16

VERSE NUMBER

_____ a. What did the Lord instruct Moses to tell Aaron?

_____ b. Why were sacrifices to be offered?

_____ c. What was to happen on the day of atonement?

Leviticus 17

_____ a. To whom were sacrifices to be offered?

_____ b. What was required for an atonement for sins?

Leviticus 18

_____ a. Which marriages were forbidden?

_____ b. What is an abomination to the Lord?

_____ c. What will happen to nations that practice sexual abominations?

Leviticus 19

_____ a. List four things Israel was commanded to do.

_____ b. What did the Lord forbid Israel to do?

Leviticus 20

_____ a. List six actions that were punishable by death. (See also Bible Dictionary, p. 604, s.v. "Adultery.")

Leviticus 21

_____ a. What was the prohibition concerning dead persons and priests? and the high priest?

_____ b. What were the restrictions about marriage for priests? for the high priest?

Leviticus 22

_____ a. What was the penalty for an unclean person who ate of the "holy things"? (Leviticus 22:3.)

_____ b. What procedure would purify an unclean person?

_____ c. What type of animals were to be sacrificed?

Leviticus 23

_____ a. What was Israel to do each weekly Sabbath?

_____ b. List the six feasts Israel was to observe.

Leviticus 24

_____ a. What was the regulation about the lamps in the tabernacle?

_____ b. What holy offering to the Lord were the priests allowed to eat? (See Leviticus 24:5a.)

_____ c. What did the Lord command be done to the person who "blasphemed the name of the Lord and cursed"? (Leviticus 24:11.)

Leviticus 25

_____ a. Which year was to be kept as a Sabbath year?

_____ b. Which year was to be one of jubilee?

_____ c. How are the events of the year of jubilee described?

_____ d. What was forbidden? (See Bible Dictionary, p. 787, s.v. "Usury.")

Leviticus 26

_____ a. What would happen to Israel if they kept the commandments?

_____ b. What would happen to Israel if they did not keep the commandments?

_____ c. What is required to obtain mercy from the Lord?

Leviticus 27

_____ a. What was Israel commanded to do?

The Fourth Book of Moses, Called NUMBERS

Introduction

See Bible Dictionary, p. 739, s.v. "Numbers."

_____ a. How did the book of Numbers get its name?

_____ b. List the four divisions in the book.

_____ c. What is remarkable about this book?

Numbers 1

_____ a. Who in each tribe were numbered in the census?

_____ b. How many were numbered?

_____ c. Where were the children of Israel to pitch their tents? (See Numbers 2:2.)

Numbers 2

_____ a. Which tribes were to camp on the east side of the "tabernacle of the congregation"? (Numbers 2:2.)

_____ b. Which tribes were to camp on the south side?

_____ c. Where were the tribe of Levi and the tabernacle to be located?

_____ d. Which tribes were to camp on the west side?

_____ e. Which tribes were to camp on the north side?

Numbers 3

VERSE NUMBER

_____ a. Who was to minister in the priest's office?

_____ b. Who was to serve in the tabernacle?

_____ c. Who were the Lord's, replacing the firstborn of all the families of Israel?

Numbers 4

VERSE NUMBER

_____ a. When the camps of Israel moved, what were Aaron and his sons to do?

_____ b. What were certain Levite families to do?

Numbers 5

VERSE NUMBER

_____ a. What was a man or a woman who had sinned to do to obtain forgiveness?

_____ b. What was the sinner to do if there was no one to recompense?

_____ c. What was the "law of jealousies"? (Numbers 5:29.)

Numbers 6

VERSE NUMBER

_____ a. What was the law of the Nazarite? (See also Bible Dictionary, p. 737, s.v. "Nazarite.")

_____ b. How were Aaron and his sons to bless Israel?

Numbers 7

_____ a. Who made offerings at the dedication of the tabernacle?

_____ b. What were the offerings to be used for?

_____ c. Who spoke to Moses when he was in the tabernacle?

Numbers 8

_____ a. How were the Levites set apart?

_____ b. Whom did the Levites replace in their dedicated service to the Lord?

_____ c. What were the Levites set apart to do?

Numbers 9

_____ a. What was Israel commanded to do again?

_____ b. What would happen to a person who was clean and able to keep the passover but did not?

_____ c. What rested upon the tabernacle by day and by night?

_____ d. What did Israel do when the cloud rested upon the tabernacle?

Numbers 10

_____ a. What were the silver trumpets used for?

_____ b. What did Israel do when the cloud was taken from the tabernacle?

_____ c. Whom did Moses want to be a guide?

Numbers 11

_____ a. Why did fire burn those in "the uttermost parts of the camp"? (Numbers 11:1.)

_____ b. Why did the children of Israel weep and complain?

_____ c. What did Moses say to the Lord when he heard the people weep?

_____ d. How did the Lord help Moses bear the burden of the people?

_____ e. Why did the Lord provide flesh for the people?

_____ f. What happened when the Spirit rested on the seventy elders?

_____ g. How did the Lord provide flesh for the people?

Numbers 12

VERSE NUMBER

_____ a. Who were Aaron and Miriam? (See Numbers 26:59.)

_____ b. Why did Aaron and Miriam speak against Moses?

_____ c. What trait did Moses have more of than any other man?

_____ d. What did the Lord say to Moses, Miriam, and Aaron? (See also Bible Dictionary, p. 754, s.v. "Prophet.")

_____ e. How did the Lord punish Miriam?

Numbers 13

VERSE NUMBER

_____ a. What did the Lord instruct Moses to do?

_____ b. What did Moses instruct the spies to do?

_____ c. What did the spies report to Moses?

_____ d. What did Caleb say to the people?

_____ e. Why were the spies afraid to go up against the people?

_____ f. Why did the spies fear the sons of Anak?

Numbers 14

VERSE NUMBER

_____ a. What did the Israelites say to Moses and Aaron?

_____ b. What did Joshua and Caleb say to the people?

_____ c. How did the congregation accept their message?

_____ d. What did Moses say to the Lord to prevent the people from being destroyed?

_____ e. Who would not be allowed to enter into the promised land?

_____ f. How long were the children of Israel to wander in the wilderness? Why? (See also Numbers 14:33b.)

_____ g. What happened to the spies who brought an evil report of the land?

_____ h. What happened to those who went to war without the Lord?

Numbers 15

VERSE NUMBER

_____ a. What was to be done with those who willfully sinned?

_____ b. What was done to the man found gathering sticks on the Sabbath day?

Numbers 16

VERSE NUMBER

_____ a. What did the company of rebels desire?

_____ b. What happened to Korah, Dathan, and Abiram?

_____ c. What happened to the two hundred fifty men who followed them?

_____ d. What did the Lord do when the congregation murmured against Moses and Aaron because of their loss?

Numbers 17

VERSE NUMBER

_____ a. Why were the twelve rods placed in the tabernacle?

_____ b. What sign was given that Aaron was the Lord's chosen servant?

_____ c. Why was Aaron's rod kept?

Numbers 18

VERSE NUMBER

_____ a. What were Aaron and his sons called to do? (See also Bible Dictionary, p. 753, s.v. "Priests.")

_____ b. What were the Levites called to do?

_____ c. How were the Levites to be supported?

Numbers 19

VERSE NUMBER

_____ a. How long would a man remain unclean after touching "the dead body of any man"? (Numbers 19:11.)

_____ b. What was to be done with those who remained unclean?

Numbers 20

VERSE NUMBER

_____ a. Who died at Kadesh?

_____ b. Why did the people complain?

_____ c. What did the Lord instruct Moses to do?

_____ d. Why were Moses and Aaron not permitted to take the people into the promised land? (See Numbers 20:12a.)

_____ e. What did the king of Edom say and do when Moses asked permission for the Israelites to pass through his land?

_____ f. Why did Aaron and his son Eleazar go up to Mount Hor? (See also Bible Dictionary, p. 702, s.v. "High Priest.")

Numbers 21

VERSE NUMBER

_____ a. Why did the Lord deliver up the Canaanites?

_____ b. Why did the people complain against God and Moses?

_____ c. How did the Lord respond?

_____ d. What remedy did the Lord provide the people?

_____ e. What was symbolized by the fiery serpent that Moses made? (See Helaman 8:13–15.)

_____ f. What did Shihon do when Israel asked for permission to pass through his land?

_____ g. What did Israel do after the battle?

46

_____ h. What did Israel do to the people of Bashan?

Numbers 22

VERSE NUMBER

_____ a. Why did Balak, king of the Moabites, request the help of Balaam?

_____ b. What did the Lord say to Balaam?

_____ c. What did Balaam tell the princes of Balak?

_____ d. What did Balak do then?

_____ e. Why did the ass disobey Balaam?

_____ f. What did the ass say to Balaam?

_____ g. How was Balaam able to see the angel?

_____ h. Upon what condition was Balaam to continue his journey?

Numbers 23

VERSE NUMBER

_____ a. What was the Lord's message that Balaam delivered to Balak?

_____ b. What was Balak's reaction?

_____ c. What was the second message that Balaam delivered to Balak?

Numbers 24

VERSE NUMBER

_____ a. What vision did Balaam receive on the top of Peor? (See also Numbers 23:28.)

_____ b. What was Balak's reaction?

_____ c. Of whom did Balaam prophesy? (See Numbers 24:17a, b.)

Numbers 25

VERSE NUMBER

_____ a. How did the chief men of Israel turn away the anger of the Lord?

_____ b. What did Phinehas, grandson of Aaron, do to stay the plague?

_____ c. How did the Lord reward Phinehas?

_____ d. Why was Israel to "vex" the Midianites? (Numbers 25:17.)

Numbers 26

_____ a. What did Moses and Eleazar do on the plains of Moab near Jericho?

_____ b. How many males twenty years and older were numbered?

_____ c. Who remained from those numbered at Sinai? Why? (See also Numbers 14:29–30.)

Numbers 27

_____ a. What was the law of inheritances?

_____ b. Why was Moses to go up to Mount Abarim?

_____ c. What did Moses request of the Lord before he was taken from the people?

_____ d. What did the Lord instruct Moses to do? (See also Numbers 27:20a.)

_____ e. How was Joshua set apart?

Numbers 28

_____ a. When were the sacrifices to be offered?

_____ b. What was prohibited on days of "holy convocation"? (Numbers 28:18, 25–26.)

Numbers 29

_____ a. At what other times were sacrifices to be offered?

_____ b. These sacrifices were to be performed in addition to what other offerings?

Numbers 30

_____ a. What was to be kept and not broken?

Who could disallow vows of daughters?

_____ c. Who could disallow vows of wives?

_____ d. In what case might a husband bear his wife's iniquity?

Numbers 31

_____ a. What did Moses send twelve thousand warriors to do?

_____ b. What happened to the possessions of the Midianites?

_____ c. What was the process of purification for soldiers and their spoils?

_____ d. How many warriors of Israel were lost?

Numbers 32

_____ a. What did the children of Reuben and Gad want to do? Why?

_____ b. What did they covenant to do?

_____ c. Half of what other tribe received their inheritance east of Jordan?

Numbers 33

_____ a. What does Numbers 33 review? (See also Map 3.)

_____ b. Why was Israel commanded to "drive out all the inhabitants of the land"? (V. 52.)

Numbers 34

_____ a. What did Moses specify in Numbers 34?

_____ b. What were the chosen princes of the tribes to do?

Numbers 35

_____ a. What were the children of Israel to give to the Levites?

_____ b. What were the cities of refuge for? (See also Numbers 35:11a.)

_____ c. What would happen to a man who threw a stone in hatred and killed another? threw a stone meaning no harm, and killed another?

_____ d. Why was death the penalty for murder? (See also v. 33b.)

Numbers 36

_____ a. Why were the daughters of Israel to marry within their own tribes?

The Fifth Book of Moses, Called DEUTERONOMY

Introduction

See Bible Dictionary, page 656, s.v. "Deuteronomy."

_____ a. What does *deuteronomy* mean?

_____ b. What is recorded in chapters 1 through 4?

_____ c. What is contained in the two parts of the second discourse?

_____ d. What does the third discourse contain?

_____ e. List three events recorded in chapters 30 through 34.

Deuteronomy 1

_____ a. What did Moses begin to do? (See also Deuteronomy 1:5a, b.)

_____ b. In Horeb, what did the Lord instruct the Israelites to do?

_____ c. How did the Lord help Moses lead the people?

_____ d. What did Moses tell the judges to do? (See also v. 17a.)

_____ e. What did Moses tell the people when they came to the mountains of the Amorites?

_____ f. What did the people say to Moses about possessing the land?

_____ g. Why did the people murmur in their tents? (See also Numbers 13:31–33.)

_____ h. What did Moses say to encourage the people?

_____ i. Why did the Lord permit only Caleb and Joshua of their generation to enter the promised land?

_____ j. What did the Lord say to Moses when the people prepared to take the land by war?

_____ k. How did the Lord respond when the Israelites were beaten and wept before him?

Deuteronomy 2

VERSE NUMBER

_____ a. What did the Lord tell Moses at Mount Seir?

_____ b. Why were the Israelites commanded not to take the land of Seir?

_____ c. Why were the Israelites commanded not to contend with the Moabites?

_____ d. How many years passed between the time the twelve spies were sent to explore the land and the time when the Lord commanded the people to pass over the brook Zered to the coast of Moab?

_____ e. Why were the Israelites commanded not to contend with the children of Ammon?

_____ f. Whose land had the Lord given to the Israelites?

_____ g. What did the Israelites request of Sihon?

_____ h. What did the Israelites do after Sihon came against them?

Deuteronomy 3

VERSE NUMBER

_____ a. What did the Lord say to Moses before the battle with the people of Bashan?

_____ b. Which three tribes shared the land that had been conquered?

_____ c. What did Moses ask of the Lord?

_____ d. What was the Lord's response? Why? (See Numbers 20:10–12; 12_b_.)

_____ e. How was Moses to help Joshua? Why?

Deuteronomy 4

VERSE NUMBER

_____ a. Why did Moses encourage the people to keep the commandments and ordinances?

_____ b. What did Moses instruct the people to do?

_____ c. What did the people see and hear at Mount Horeb?

_____ d. Why did the Lord not show himself to the children of Israel? (See D&C 84:23–24.)

_____ e. What did Moses prophesy?

_____ f. Why did God perform so many miracles and speak to the people?

_____ g. What were the people to know and consider in their hearts?

_____ h. What did Moses do when he finished speaking? Why? (See also Deuteronomy 4:41a.)

Deuteronomy 5

VERSE NUMBER

_____ a. Why did Moses call together all of Israel to listen to him?

_____ b. What covenant did the Lord make with the people in Horeb? (See Exodus 20:1–17.)

_____ c. What did the Lord say to the people from the mount?

_____ d. What had the people seen that day?

_____ e. Why did the people ask Moses to go before the Lord and then return to tell them the Lord's message?

_____ f. Why were the people to keep the commandments?

Deuteronomy 6

VERSE NUMBER

_____ a. Why did Moses teach the people the commandments and ordinances? (See also Deuteronomy 6:1b.)

_____ b. How should we love the Lord?

_____ c. What were the people to do with the instructions? (See also vv. 8b and 9a.)

_____ d. Under what circumstances would the people be likely to forget the Lord?

_____ e. List five things the people were instructed to do.

_____ f. List two things the people were instructed not to do.

_____ g. What were the people to say to their children when they asked the meaning of the commandments and the ordinances? (See also v. 1b.)

Deuteronomy 7

_____ a. What was Israel to do to the seven nations of Canaan?

_____ b. Why were the Israelites commanded not to intermarry with the Canaanites?

_____ c. Why were the Israelites to keep themselves free from idolatry?

_____ d. Why had the Lord chosen Israel and brought them out of bondage?

_____ e. How would the Lord bless Israel if they were faithful?

_____ f. Why were the Israelites forbidden to take gold and silver from the graven images of the Canaanites' gods?

Deuteronomy 8

_____ a. Why did the Lord lead Israel in the wilderness for forty years?

_____ b. Why were the people fed manna?

_____ c. What happened to the Israelites' clothing in forty years? (See Deuteronomy 8:4a.)

_____ d. Why did the Lord chasten Israel?

_____ e. What did the Lord provide for his people?

_____ f. What were the people to beware of? Why?

Deuteronomy 9

_____ a. What was Israel about to do?

_____ b. What should the people not say in their heart?

_____ c. Why was Israel given possession of the land?

_____ d. For how many days did Moses fast before he received the two tables of stone?

_____ e. List two occasions when the people rebelled against the Lord.

_____ f. What did Moses say to the Lord to prevent Israel from being destroyed?

Deuteronomy 10

_____ a. What did the Lord write on the first tables of stone that he did not write on the second tables? (See Deuteronomy 10:2b.)

_____ b. What did the Lord write on the second tables of stone?

_____ c. Where did Moses put the two tables of stone?

_____ d. What did the Lord set apart the tribe of Levi to do?

_____ e. What did the Lord require of the Israelites as they entered the promised land?

Deuteronomy 11

_____ a. What had the adults in Israel seen the Lord do?

_____ b. What did the Lord promise he would do if the people kept all the commandments?

_____ c. How was the land of Canaan different from the land of Egypt?

_____ d. What would the Lord do if the people worshiped other gods?

_____ e. What did Moses set before the people? (See also D&C 130:20–21.)

Deuteronomy 12

_____ a. What were the people told to destroy?

_____ b. Where were the people to offer their burnt offering?

_____ c. What were they to do with the blood of the animals they ate?

_____ d. Why were the people to "observe and hear" all the words of Moses? (Deuteronomy 12:28.)

_____ e. What were the Israelites to be careful not to do?

_____ f. What were the Israelites to be careful to do?

Deuteronomy 13

VERSE NUMBER

_____ a. Why does the Lord allow false prophets to give signs or wonders?

_____ b. In verse 4 what was Israel told to do?

_____ c. What were the Israelites to do to those who sought to lead others after false gods? Why?

_____ d. What were the Israelites to do to cities that became corrupted?

_____ e. What were the Israelites to do with the property of corrupted cities? Why? (See also Deuteronomy 13:17a.)

Deuteronomy 14

VERSE NUMBER

_____ a. What did the Lord choose the children of Israel to be?

_____ b. What kind of beasts were the Israelites allowed to eat?

_____ c. What were they allowed to eat from the waters?

_____ d. What were the people to tithe?

_____ e. Who was not to be forsaken? Why?

_____ f. What was to be done with the tithing of the people?

Deuteronomy 15

VERSE NUMBER

_____ a. What was to be released at the end of every seven years? Why? (See Deuteronomy 15:4a.)

_____ b. What was required of the people to be greatly blessed in the land?

_____ c. How would Israel be blessed in dealing with other nations?

_____ d. What were the people to do with the poor within their gates?

_____ e. What was the master to do for the servant who decided to leave after six years?

_____ f. What was the master to do with a servant who decided to stay after six years?

Deuteronomy 16

VERSE NUMBER

_____ a. What did the Feast of Unleavened Bread, or the Passover, commemorate? (See Bible Dictionary, p. 672, s.v. "Feasts.")

_____ b. What was the Feast of Weeks? (See Bible Dictionary, p. 672, s.v. "Feasts.")

_____ c. What was celebrated by the Feast of Tabernacles? (See Bible Dictionary, p. 672, s.v. "Feasts.")

_____ d. When were all males to appear before the Lord?

_____ e. Why were the judges not to accept gifts? (See Deuteronomy 16:19, 19a.)

Deuteronomy 17

VERSE NUMBER

_____ a. What was to be done with those who worshiped false gods?

_____ b. Who was to throw the first stone?

_____ c. What were the people to do when difficult cases were to be judged?

_____ d. What was to happen to the man who did not obey the priest?

_____ e. Who would choose a king over the people?

_____ f. What was the king forbidden to do?

_____ g. What was the king to read "all the days of his life"? Why? (Deuteronomy 17:19.)

Deuteronomy 18

VERSE NUMBER

_____ a. How were the Levites to be supported?

_____ b. Who was the prophet who would be raised up? (See Deuteronomy 18:15b, 18a.)

_____ c. How were the people to know if a prophet spoke for the Lord?

Deuteronomy 19

_____ a. How was the person protected who unintentionally killed his neighbor?

_____ b. What was required of the people for them to have three more cities of refuge?

_____ c. What was to happen to the person who intentionally killed his neighbor and fled to a city of refuge?

_____ d. How many witnesses were required to establish a matter?

_____ e. What was to be done to a false witness?

_____ f. What was the code of justice for Israel? (See Deuteronomy 19:21a.)

Deuteronomy 20

_____ a. What was the priest to say to the army before the battle?

_____ b. List four reasons why a soldier was allowed to return home.

_____ c. What was to happen when peace was offered to a distant city and the city accepted the offer? rejected the offer?

_____ d. What was Israel to do to the inhabitants of the cities in the land that the Lord had given them? Why?

Deuteronomy 21

_____ a. What were the people to do if a person was found slain by an unknown person? Why?

_____ b. What was to happen to sons who were stubborn and rebellious?

Deuteronomy 22

_____ a. What was to happen to property that was found and the owner was known? the owner was unknown?

_____ b. What was to happen if a man married and then claimed his wife was not a virgin when she was a virgin? when she was not a virgin?

_____ c. What was to happen to the man and the married woman who committed adultery? (See also Leviticus 20:10.)

Deuteronomy 23

VERSE NUMBER

_____ a. Why was Israel not to abhor an Edomite or an Egyptian? (See also Genesis 25:30.)

_____ b. Why was there to be no unclean thing in the army camp?

_____ c. What could a neighbor do in another's vineyard?

Deuteronomy 24

VERSE NUMBER

_____ a. What was a man not to do for one year after being married? Why?

_____ b. What was to happen to a kidnapper?

_____ c. When was the poor servant to receive his wages?

_____ d. How did the Lord provide for the poor?

Deuteronomy 25

VERSE NUMBER

_____ a. What was a man to do with his brother's widow if she had no children? Why?

_____ b. What was Israel commanded to have that were "perfect and just"? (Deuteronomy 25:15.) Why?

_____ c. What was Israel to do to Amalek? Why? (See also Exodus 17:13–16; 1 Chronicles 4:42–43.)

Deuteronomy 26

VERSE NUMBER

_____ a. What was to be delivered to the priest when Israel arrived in the new land?

_____ b. What was to be said before the Lord?

_____ c. What was to be said before the Lord after the tithing was paid?

_____ d. How were the children of Israel to keep and do the commandments of the Lord?

_____ e. What had the people testified to the Lord?

_____ f. What had the Lord testified to the people?

Deuteronomy 27

_____ a. What were the Israelites to do on the day they crossed over Jordan?

_____ b. What had the people become on the day they crossed over Jordan?

_____ c. What were they commanded to do?

_____ d. For what offenses would a man be cursed? (See also Bible Dictionary, p. 607, s.v. "Amen.")

Deuteronomy 28

_____ a. Why would Israel be blessed by the Lord?

_____ b. What were the promised blessings?

_____ c. Why would Israel be cursed by the Lord?

_____ d. What were the promised cursings?

_____ e. What would happen if Israel chose not to serve the Lord?

Deuteronomy 29

_____ a. Where was the covenant made?

_____ b. Why did the Lord make this covenant with Israel?

_____ c. What would happen to those who broke this covenant? (See also Deuteronomy 29:19a.)

Deuteronomy 30

_____ a. When would the Lord gather Israel?

_____ b. Where would Israel be gathered?

_____ c. Upon whom would the Lord put "all these curses"? (Deuteronomy 30:7.)

_____ d. What did Moses say was "in [their] mouth, and in [their] heart"? (V. 14.)

_____ e. What did Moses set before the people that day?

_____ f. What did Moses call heaven and earth to do?

List three things you need to do to be blessed by the Lord.

Deuteronomy 31

VERSE NUMBER

_____ a. How old was Moses?

_____ b. What did Moses say about taking the land the Lord gave them?

_____ c. What did Moses say to Joshua "in the sight of all Israel"? (Deuteronomy 31:7.)

_____ d. When was the law to be read to the people? Why?

_____ e. What did the Lord say to Moses in the tabernacle about Israel's future?

_____ f. Why did the Lord give Moses a song to teach the children of Israel?

_____ g. What did the Lord say to Joshua?

_____ h. What did Moses say to the Levites?

Deuteronomy 32

VERSE NUMBER

_____ a. List six things the song of Moses acclaimed.

_____ b. Who spoke the words of this song to the people? (See also v. 44b.)

_____ c. What did the Lord command Moses to do? Why?

Deuteronomy 33

_____ a. What did Moses do just before his death?

_____ b. Who was to teach the Lord's judgments and his law?

_____ c. Who shall gather Israel in the latter days?

Deuteronomy 34

_____ a. What did the Lord show Moses?

_____ b. What did the Lord say to Moses?

_____ c. How old was Moses when he fled from Egypt to Midian? (See Acts 7:23–29.)

_____ d. How old was Moses when he returned to Egypt and met with Pharaoh? (See Acts 7:30; Exodus 7:7.)

_____ e. How old was Moses when he was translated? (See also Bible Dictionary, p. 734, s.v. "Moses.")

_____ f. How long did the people mourn for Moses?

_____ g. Who was their new leader? Why?

_____ h. What had Moses done to become a great prophet?

_____ i. What had Moses sought diligently to do? Why? (See D&C 84:23.)

_____ j. How were Moses' efforts received by the people? by the Lord? (See D&C 84:24.)

_____ k. What did the Lord take from the midst of the people? (See D&C 84:25.)

The Book of JOSHUA

Introduction

See Bible Dictionary, page 718, s.v. "Joshua, Book of."

_____ a. Why is the book called the book of Joshua?

_____ b. List the three main parts of this book.

Joshua 1

VERSE NUMBER

_____ a. What instruction did the Lord give to Joshua?

_____ b. When were the men of the tribes of Reuben and Gad and half the tribe of Manasseh to return to their families?

_____ c. To what extent did these men support Joshua?

Joshua 2

VERSE NUMBER

_____ a. Where did Joshua send his two spies? (See also Map 4.)

_____ b. How did Rahab save the spies from the king?

_____ c. What had happened to Rahab's people when they heard that the Israelites were coming? Why?

_____ d. What did Rahab require of the two spies?

_____ e. What did the men agree to do?

_____ f. What was Rahab to do when the Israelites came?

Joshua 3

VERSE NUMBER

_____ a. What were the people to do when they saw the ark?

_____ b. Why were the people to sanctify themselves? (See also Joshua 3:5a.)

_____ c. How would the Lord magnify Joshua in the sight of all Israel? (See also Joshua 4:14.)

Joshua 4

VERSE NUMBER

_____ a. Why was a man from each tribe to take up a stone?

_____ b. What happened to the River Jordan when the priests came out?

Joshua 5

VERSE NUMBER

_____ a. What happened to the hearts of the Amorite and the Canaanite kings? Why?

_____ b. Why were all the males circumcised?

_____ c. What gift of God ceased after the Israelites passed over Jordan?

_____ d. Whom did Joshua see while he was "by Jericho"? (Joshua 5:13.)

Joshua 6

_____ a. How did the Israelites capture the city of Jericho? (See also Map 4.)

_____ b. What did Joshua caution the people against doing? (See also Joshua 6:18a.)

_____ c. What happened to Rahab, her family, and her possessions?

_____ d. What did Joshua declare "as by an oath"? (See also v. 26a.)

Joshua 7

_____ a. What did Achan do to anger the Lord? (See also Joshua 6:18a.)

_____ b. Why was the army of Israel defeated by the men of Ai?

_____ c. What had Achan taken?

_____ d. What happened to Achan and all his possessions?

Joshua 8

_____ a. What did the Lord instruct the people to do with the spoils of Ai?

_____ b. How did Israel take the city of Ai?

_____ c. What happened to the inhabitants of the city?

_____ d. What happened to the king of Ai?

_____ e. What did Joshua read to the Israelites?

Joshua 9

_____ a. What did all the kings in the land do when they heard of the Israelites' success?

_____ b. What did the inhabitants of Gibeon do? Why? (See also Joshua 9:7a.)

_____ c. What agreement did Joshua make with them?

_____ d. What did Joshua make them be? Why?

Joshua 10

_____ a. Why did King Adoni-zedek call upon the other kings to smite Gibeon?

_____ b. What did the men of Gibeon ask Joshua to do?

_____ c. What did the Lord say to Joshua?

_____ d. How did most of the Amorites die that day?

_____ e. What did Joshua command to stand still? Why?

_____ f. What happened to the Amorite kings?

_____ g. What did the Israelites do to "all that breathed" in the land? (Joshua 10:40.)

Joshua 11

_____ a. What did the Lord tell Israel he would do to the army?

_____ b. How strictly had Joshua followed the commands of the Lord through Moses?

_____ c. Who were the only people to make peace with Israel?

Joshua 12

_____ a. How many kings were conquered by Israel?

Joshua 13

_____ a. Whose inheritance was confirmed?

_____ b. How much land remained to be possessed?

Joshua 14

_____ a. What method was used to divide the land among the tribes? (See also Map 5.)

_____ b. Which tribe was divided into two tribes?

_____ c. Why was Caleb given Hebron for an inheritance?

Joshua 15

_____ a. What city was included in the inheritance of Judah?

_____ b. Why did the Jebusites dwell with Judah in Jerusalem?

Joshua 16

_____ a. Locate on Map 5 the places where the children of Ephraim and Manasseh settled.

_____ b. What did the Canaanites do who dwelt in Gezer? (See also Joshua 16:10b.)

Joshua 17

_____ a. Which two tribes received additional inheritances?

_____ b. What did Joshua say to the house of Joseph?

Joshua 18

_____ a. What was set up at Shiloh?

_____ b. How did the tribe of Benjamin receive their inheritance?

_____ c. How many cities did the children of Benjamin receive?

Joshua 19

_____ a. How did the remaining six tribes receive their inheritances?

Joshua 20

_____ a. What did the Lord tell Joshua to do? Why?

_____ b. What was a person to do who killed another by accident?

_____ c. When was such a person allowed to return to his home?

Joshua 21

_____ a. How many "cities with their suburbs" did the Levites receive? (Headnote to Joshua 21.)

_____ b. What did the Lord do for Israel?

Joshua 22

_____ a. Whom did Joshua call together?

_____ b. What did Joshua say to them?

_____ c. What did Joshua tell them to take diligent heed to do?

_____ d. What did they build on "the borders of Jordan"? (Joshua 22:10.)

_____ e. What did the rest of the tribes prepare to do?

_____ f. What reason was given for building the altar?

_____ g. How did the other tribes receive this explanation?

Joshua 23

_____ a. What did Joshua say the Lord would do for Israel?

_____ b. What did Joshua exhort Israel to do? Why?

_____ c. What did the people know in their hearts?

_____ d. When would the Lord's anger be kindled against Israel?

_____ e. What would the Lord do in his anger?

Joshua 24

_____ a. What did Joshua review with the leadership of Israel?

_____ b. What did Joshua encourage them to do?

_____ c. What ultimatum did Joshua deliver to Israel?

_____ d. How did the people respond?

_____ e. What did Israel promise to do?

_____ f. How old was Joshua when he died?

The Book of JUDGES

Introduction

See Bible Dictionary, page 719, s.v. "Judges, Book of."

_____ a. What do the book of Judges and the book of Ruth contain?

_____ b. What are the three parts of the book of Judges?

_____ c. What does the book of Judges help us to understand?

_____ d. How were the tribes united?

_____ e. When did Israel feel the need for a single leader to unite the tribes?

_____ f. What did each person do when there was no king?

Judges 1

_____ a. Who united with Judah to fight the Canaanites?

b. What did they do to Adoni-bezek?

_____ c. What did Adoni-bezek say?

_____ d. To whom did Caleb give his daughter? Why?

_____ e. How successful was Judah in fighting the Canaanites?

_____ f. What did Israel do to the Canaanites who were not removed from the land?

Judges 2

VERSE NUMBER

_____ a. What did the angel of the Lord say to Israel?

_____ b. What was the response of the people?

_____ c. How long did the people serve the Lord?

_____ d. How did the new generation anger the Lord?

_____ e. How did the Lord deal with Israel?

_____ f. What was the Israelites' response to the judges?

_____ g. Why did the Lord raise up judges to deliver them from their enemies? (See Judges 2:18a.)

_____ h. What did Israel do when their judges died?

_____ i. Why did Israel fail to destroy all the Canaanites? (See also Judges 4:1–4; 1 Nephi 2:23–24.)

Judges 3

VERSE NUMBER

_____ a. What did the Israelites do while they were living among the heathen nations?

_____ b. How long did the children of Israel serve the king of Mesopotamia?

_____ c. How were the Israelites freed?

_____ d. What did the Israelites do after forty years?

_____ e. What happened to them?

_____ f. Why did the Lord deliver Israel from the king of Moab?

_____ g. How did Ehud kill the king?

_____ h. How long did the land rest?

_____ i. What did Shamgar do?

Judges 4

VERSE NUMBER

_____ a. What did the Israelites do again after Ehud died?

_____ b. Who judged Israel during their Canaanite captivity?

_____ c. Upon what condition would Barak do as Deborah requested?

_____ d. How did the Lord help Barak? (See Judges 4:15a.)

_____ e. What happened to the army of Sisera?

_____ f. How did Sisera, the captain of the king of Canaan, die?

Judges 5

VERSE NUMBER

_____ a. Why did Deborah and Barak sing the song of praise?

Judges 6

VERSE NUMBER

_____ a. What did the children of Israel do "in the sight of the Lord"? (Judges 6:1.)

_____ b. What happened to them?

_____ c. How was Gideon called to lead the people?

_____ d. What did Gideon say to the "angel of the Lord"?

_____ e. What sign did the angel give to Gideon?

_____ f. Why did Gideon destroy the altar of Baal at night?

_____ g. What did Gideon's father say to the men who came to take Gideon?

_____ h. What signs were given Gideon that he should lead Israel?

Judges 7

_____ a. Why did the Lord tell Gideon there were too many warriors?

_____ b. Why did twenty-two thousand people go home?

_____ c. How many people did the Lord choose to stay?

_____ d. How did Gideon obtain victory?

Judges 8

VERSE NUMBER

_____ a. What did Gideon ask of the men of Succoth and Penuel?

_____ b. How was he received?

_____ c. How many of the enemy remained?

_____ d. How many had been destroyed?

_____ e. What did Gideon do to the enemy who remained?

_____ f. Why did Gideon slay Zebah and Zalmunna?

_____ g. What was Gideon's reply when "the men of Israel" asked him to be king? (Judges 8:22.)

_____ h. What did Gideon request of the men of Israel?

_____ i. What did Gideon make? Why did it become a snare to him?

_____ j. How many sons did Gideon have?

_____ k. What did the children of Israel do "as soon as Gideon was dead"? (V. 33.)

Judges 9

VERSE NUMBER

_____ a. What did Abimelech do to his brothers? (See also Judges 8:31.)

_____ b. Why was Jotham not killed?

_____ c. What did Jotham do after telling the men of Shechem a fable of the trees choosing a king? Why?

_____ d. How did the men of Shechem deal "treacherously with Abimelech"? (Judges 9:23.)

_____ e. What did Abimelech do to the men of Shechem?

_____ f. How did Abimelech die?

_____ g. Why were Abimelech and the men of Shechem destroyed?

Judges 10

_____ a. How did the children of Israel do evil "in the sight of the Lord"? (Judges 10:6.)

_____ b. What did the Lord do to them?

_____ c. What did the Lord say when they cried unto him for help?

_____ d. How did the children of Israel respond?

_____ e. How did the people of Gilead choose their leader?

Judges 11

_____ a. Who was Jephthah?

_____ b. How did Jephthah become the Israelites' leader?

_____ c. Why did the people of Ammon come to fight with Israel?

_____ d. What did Jephthah reply? (See also D&C 64:10–11.)

_____ e. What did the Spirit of the Lord do when the king "hearkened not unto the words of Jephthah"? (Judges 11:28.)

_____ f. What vow did Jephthah take before the Lord?

_____ g. What did the Lord and Jephthah do to the children of Ammon?

_____ h. How was Jephthah's vow fulfilled?

Judges 12

_____ a. Why did the men of Ephraim gather against Jephthah?

_____ b. How many Ephraimites were killed?

_____ c. How long did Jephthah judge Israel?

Judges 13

_____ a. Why did the Lord deliver the children of Israel to the Philistines for forty years?

_____ b. What message did the angel deliver to the wife of Manoah? (See also Bible Dictionary, p. 737, s.v. "Nazarite.")

_____ c. What did Manoah request of God?

_____ d. What did the angel of the Lord say in his second visit?

_____ e. How did Manoah know "the man of God" was an angel of the Lord? (Judges 13:8.)

_____ f. What was the child's name?

Judges 14

_____ a. Why did Samson ask his parents to get a daughter of the Philistines to be his wife?

_____ b. What did Samson do to the young lion?

_____ c. What was in the carcass of the lion when Samson returned?

_____ d. What riddle did Samson give?

_____ e. How were the Philistines able to answer the riddle?

_____ f. How did Samson pay his wager?

Judges 15

_____ a. What had Samson's father-in-law done with Samson's wife?

_____ b. What did Samson do with the three hundred foxes?

_____ c. What did the Philistines do to Samson's wife? (See also Judges 15:6b.)

_____ d. What did Samson do to the Philistines before he went to live "in the top of the rock Etam"? (V. 8.)

_____ e. What did Samson do to the Philistines with the "jawbone of an ass"? (V. 15.)

_____ f. How long did Samson judge Israel?

Judges 16

_____ a. Why did Delilah seek to know the secret of Samson's strength?

_____ b. Why did Samson tell Delilah the secret to his strength?

_____ c. What did the Philistines do to Samson?

_____ d. Why did the Philistines gather together?

_____ e. How did Samson die?

Judges 17

VERSE NUMBER

_____ a. Why did Micah's mother give the founder two hundred shekels of silver?

_____ b. What did Micah do?

_____ c. What did every man do in those days?

_____ d. Why did Micah think the Lord would do him good?

Judges 18

VERSE NUMBER

_____ a. What did the tribe of Dan seek?

_____ b. Why did they send out five men?

_____ c. What did the five men find in Laish?

_____ d. What did the army take from Micah?

_____ e. What did the children of Dan do to the city of Laish?

_____ f. Why did no one help the people of Laish?

_____ g. What name did the Danites call the new city?

_____ h. What did the Danites do with Micah's graven image?

73

Judges 19

_____ a. Why did the Levite go to the house of his father-in-law?

_____ b. How did the father-in-law receive the Levite?

_____ c. Why did the Levite and his concubine stop in Gibeah?

_____ d. How did the old man treat them?

_____ e. What did the men of the city do?

_____ f. What did the Levite do with his concubine?

Judges 20

_____ a. How many "footmen" were gathered?

_____ b. What did the Levite say to them?

_____ c. In what manner were the men of Israel gathered against the city? (See Judges 20:11a.)

_____ d. What message did the tribes of Israel deliver to the tribe of Benjamin?

_____ e. How did the children of Benjamin respond?

_____ f. What did the children of Israel ask the Lord before the first day of battle?

_____ g. What did the children of Israel ask the Lord before the second day of battle?

_____ h. What did the children of Israel ask the Lord before the third day of battle?

_____ i. How many men of the tribe of Benjamin were left alive?

Judges 21

_____ a. Why did the people weep at the house of God?

_____ b. What oath was made at the gathering at Mizpeh? (See also Judges 20:1.)

_____ c. How did the Israelites provide four hundred wives for the men of Benjamin?

_____ d. How did the men of Benjamin who did not have a wife get one?

_____ e. What did every man in Israel do in those days?

The Book of RUTH

Introduction

See Bible Dictionary, page 764, s.v. "Ruth."

_____ a. What is the book of Ruth?

_____ b. What does the story of Ruth illustrate?

Ruth 1

VERSE NUMBER

_____ a. Why did Elimelech and Naomi go to Moab?

_____ b. Who had died in Naomi's family?

_____ c. Why did Naomi return from Moab?

_____ d. What did Ruth say to Naomi when Naomi asked Ruth to leave?

Ruth 2

VERSE NUMBER

_____ a. Who was Boaz? (See also Ruth 2:1a.)

_____ b. Why did Ruth glean ears of corn in the field of Boaz?

_____ c. What did Boaz say to Ruth?

_____ d. Why had Ruth found grace in the sight of Boaz?

_____ e. How much barley had Ruth gleaned? (See Bible Dictionary, p. 665, s.v. "Ephah.")

Ruth 3

VERSE NUMBER

_____ a. What did Naomi tell Ruth to do?

_____ b. What did Boaz promise Ruth? Why?

Ruth 4

_____ a. What did the kinsman tell Boaz about Ruth and about redeeming the land?

_____ b. What did the elders witness that day?

_____ c. What was the name of the son born of Ruth?

_____ d. Who was the son of Obed? the grandson?

The First Book of SAMUEL

Introduction

See Bible Dictionary, page 769, s.v. "Samuel, Books of."

_____ a. In which Bible are the books of Samuel one book? two books?

_____ b. What period of history is covered by the books of Samuel?

_____ c. Why do various accounts of the same event differ?

_____ d. What did the author use in writing the books?

---

1 Samuel 1

_____ a. Why was Hannah sad?

_____ b. What vow did Hannah make to the Lord?

_____ c. What did Eli the priest say to her at first? Why?

_____ d. What did Eli answer her?

_____ e. What did Hannah name her son?

_____ f. For how long was Samuel lent to the Lord?

1 Samuel 2

_____ a. What did Hannah say in her prayers? (See also 1 Samuel 2:1c.)

_____ b. What did Samuel do? (See v. 11a.)

_____ c. What did the sons of Eli do to offend the Lord?

_____ d. What did Hannah do for Samuel?

_____ e. How was Hannah blessed?

_____ f. With whom was Samuel in favor?

_____ g. Why was the Lord angry with Eli? (See v. 29a.)

_____ h. What was to happen to Eli's two sons?

_____ i. Whom was the Lord raising up to replace Eli as his priest?

1 Samuel 3

_____ a. Why was the word of the Lord "precious in those days"? (1 Samuel 3:1.)

_____ b. Why did Samuel go to Eli when the Lord called him?

_____ c. What did Eli tell Samuel to do?

_____ d. Why was the Lord about to destroy Eli's house?

_____ e. Who knew that Samuel was a prophet of the Lord?

1 Samuel 4

_____ a. Why did the people take the ark of the covenant from Shiloh?

_____ b. What did the Philistines say when they heard the shout of the Israelites? Why?

_____ c. What happened to the ark of God?

_____ d. How old was Eli when Israel lost the ark of God?

_____ e. How did Eli die?

---

1 Samuel 5

_____ a. What did the Philistines in Ashdod do with the ark?

_____ b. Why did the Philistines take the ark to Gath?

_____ c. What happened to the people in the cities where the ark of God was taken? (See also 1 Samuel 5:6a.)

---

1 Samuel 6

_____ a. What did the Philistines do with the ark?

_____ b. How many Israelites of Beth-shemish were slain? Why?

---

1 Samuel 7

_____ a. What was required of the Israelites for them to be free of the Philistines?

_____ b. What did the Israelites do?

_____ c. What did the children of Israel ask Samuel to do?

_____ d. Who was "the hand of the Lord" against "all the days of Samuel"? (1 Samuel 7:13.)

---

1 Samuel 8

_____ a. What did Samuel do with his sons when he became old?

_____ b. What evil did his sons do?

_____ c. What did the elders of Israel desire of Samuel? (See also Mosiah 29.)

_____ d. What did the Lord tell Samuel to do?

_____ e. What did Samuel tell the Israelites about their future king?

_____ f. What would the Lord do when the people cried to him?

_____ g. What did the people desire of Samuel? Why?

_____ h. What did the Lord tell Samuel to do?

---

1 Samuel 9

VERSE NUMBER

_____ a. What qualities did Saul have?

_____ b. Why did Saul visit Samuel?

_____ c. What had the Lord told Samuel about Saul?

_____ d. What did Saul say when he was called to be king?

---

1 Samuel 10

VERSE NUMBER

_____ a. What did Samuel do for Saul? Why?

_____ b. What would happen to Saul when he met "a company of prophets"? (1 Samuel 10:5.)

_____ c. What happened to Saul when he left Samuel?

_____ d. What did the Israelites say when Samuel announced that Saul was king?

_____ e. Who went with Saul to his home?

_____ f. What did Saul do when the children of Belial brought him no presents? (See also 1 Samuel 10:27b.)

---

1 Samuel 11

VERSE NUMBER

_____ a. Upon what condition would Nahash the Ammonite refrain from destroying Jabesh-gilead?

_____ b. How did Saul unify Israel to fight?

_____ c. To what extent were the Ammonites scattered?

_____ d. What did the Israelites do with Saul in Gilgal?

---

1 Samuel 12

VERSE NUMBER

_____ a. What was the Lord witness to?

79

_____ b. What did Samuel rehearse to all Israel?

_____ c. What blessing and what cursing did Samuel give the people?

_____ d. What wickedness had the people done?

_____ e. What are vain things unable to do?

_____ f. What did Samuel counsel the people to do?

1 Samuel 13

VERSE NUMBER

_____ a. How many men did Saul choose after two years?

_____ b. Why did the Philistines gather to fight against Israel?

_____ c. What did many of the Israelites do?

_____ d. Why did Saul offer a sacrifice to the Lord?

_____ e. What did the Lord do? (See also 1 Chronicles 10:13–14, 14a.)

_____ f. Why did the Israelites lack swords and spears?

1 Samuel 14

VERSE NUMBER

_____ a. What did Jonathan do?

_____ b. What happened in the army of the Philistines? (See 1 Samuel 14:20b.)

_____ c. What did Saul command the people to refrain from doing? Why?

_____ d. What did Jonathan do when he saw the honey? (See also v. 27a.)

_____ e. Who rescued Jonathan from being put to death? (See also v. 45a.)

_____ f. What did Saul do to all the enemies of Israel? (See also Map 6.)

_____ g. What did Saul do when he saw any strong or valiant man?

1 Samuel 15

VERSE NUMBER

_____ a. What was the Lord's message that Samuel gave to Saul?

_____ b. What evil thing had Saul done? (See 1 Samuel 15:11a.)

_____ c. What did Samuel do all that night?

_____ d. What did Saul say upon greeting Samuel?

_____ e. What is better than sacrifice and "the fat of rams"? (V. 22.)

_____ f. What crimes are rebellion and stubbornness like?

_____ g. Why was Saul rejected by the Lord as king?

_____ h. Why had Saul failed to destroy all the animals?

_____ i. Why did Samuel slay Agag?

_____ j. Why did Samuel stay away from Saul? (See also v. 35a.)

---

1 Samuel 16

VERSE NUMBER

_____ a. Why did the Lord tell Samuel to go to Bethlehem?

_____ b. What is the difference between how a man looks on someone and how the Lord looks?

_____ c. Which of Jesse's sons did the Lord choose to be king?

_____ d. What came upon David "from that day forward"? (1 Samuel 16:13.)

_____ e. What happened to Saul? (See v. 14c.)

_____ f. What did Saul's servants say to Saul? (See v. 15a.)

_____ g. Why did Saul send for David?

---

1 Samuel 17

VERSE NUMBER

_____ a. What did Goliath say to the army of Israel?

_____ b. What was the reaction of the Israelite army?

_____ c. For how many days did Goliath present himself?

_____ d. Why did David return to the army of Israel?

81

_____ e. What reward did Saul promise the man who killed Goliath?

_____ f. What did David say to the men who stood by him?

_____ g. What did David say to Saul?

_____ h. What did David take with him to battle?

_____ i. What did Goliath say to David?

_____ j. What did David say to Goliath?

_____ k. How was Goliath killed?

_____ l. What did the men of Israel do?

---

1 Samuel 18

_____ a. How did Saul's son Jonathan receive David?

_____ b. How did David act as a servant of Saul?

_____ c. How was David accepted?

_____ d. What aroused Saul's jealousy of David?

_____ e. What did Saul try to do to David?

_____ f. Why was Saul afraid of David?

_____ g. Why did Saul consent to give his daughter Michal as a wife to David?

_____ h. What dowry did Saul ask of David? Why?

_____ i. Why was David's name adored? (See also 1 Samuel 18:30a.)

---

1 Samuel 19

_____ a. What did Saul say to his son Jonathan and to all his servants?

_____ b. What did Jonathan say to Saul?

_____ c. What did Saul do?

_____ d. Why did David flee from Saul? (See also 1 Samuel 19:9a.)

_____ e. To whom did David flee?

---

1 Samuel 20

VERSE NUMBER

_____ a. What did David ask Jonathan to do?

_____ b. By what sign was David to know if he should flee or stay?

_____ c. What did Saul command Jonathan to do?

_____ d. What covenant did David and Jonathan make?

---

1 Samuel 21

VERSE NUMBER

_____ a. What did David take from the priest at Nob?

_____ b. What did David do in Gath because of his fear of the king?

---

1 Samuel 22

VERSE NUMBER

_____ a. Who came to help David?

_____ b. What did David do to protect his parents?

_____ c. What did Saul do to the priest Ahimelech who helped David and to all the house of Ahimelech's father? Why?

---

1 Samuel 23

VERSE NUMBER

_____ a. Why did David inquire of the Lord?

_____ b. How did David save the inhabitants of Keilah?

_____ c. What did the Lord tell David about Saul and the men of Keilah?

_____ d. Why did Saul not go to Keilah?

_____ e. What did Jonathan say to David?

_____ f. What did Saul tell the Ziphites who came to him?

_____ g. Why did Saul stop pursuing David?

---

1 Samuel 24

VERSE NUMBER

_____ a. Why did David feel remorse for cutting off the skirt of Saul's robe? (See also 1 Samuel 24:4a.)

_____ b. What did David say to Saul? (See also D&C 64:9–11.)

_____ c. What did Saul say to David?

_____ d. What did David swear to Saul?

---

1 Samuel 25

VERSE NUMBER

_____ a. Why did all the Israelites gather to lament?

_____ b. Describe Abigail.

_____ c. Describe Nabal. (See also 1 Samuel 25:3a, 25a.)

_____ d. Why did David send ten young men to Nabal?

_____ e. How were these young men received by Nabal? (See also v. 14b.)

_____ f. What did Abigail say to David?

_____ g. How did David receive Abigail's message and gift?

_____ h. When did Nabal die?

_____ i. What did David say when he heard of Nabal's death?

_____ j. What did David do after Nabal died?

---

1 Samuel 26

VERSE NUMBER

_____ a. How many men did Saul take with him to slay David?

_____ b. What did David say when Abishai wanted to kill Saul?

_____ c. What did David and Abishai take with them?

_____ d. What did David say to Abner?

_____ e. What did David say to Saul?

_____ f. How did Saul receive David's message?

---

1 Samuel 27

VERSE NUMBER

_____ a. Who went with David to Achish, king of Gath?

_____ b. What did David ask of Achish?

_____ c. What did Achish say after David had made his raids? (See also 1 Samuel 27:10a.)

---

1 Samuel 28

VERSE NUMBER

_____ a. What did Achish desire of David?

_____ b. Whom had Saul banished from the land? (See also 1 Samuel 28:3a.)

_____ c. Why did Saul inquire of the Lord?

_____ d. Why did Saul seek "a woman that hath a familiar spirit"? (V. 7.)

_____ e. To whom did Saul want to speak? (See also Bible Dictionary, p. 768, s.v. "Samuel.")

_____ f. What did Saul say to Samuel?

_____ g. To whom had the Lord given the kingdom? Why?

_____ h. What did Samuel say would happen the next day?

---

1 Samuel 29

VERSE NUMBER

_____ a. What did the princes of the Philistines say to Achish?

_____ b. What did Achish say to David?

_____ c. What did David reply?

_____ d. What did Achish answer?

1 Samuel 30

_____ a. What did the Amalekites do to Ziklag before David returned?

_____ b. What did David and his men do when they returned?

_____ c. How did David know what to do?

_____ d. Upon what condition did the young Egyptian agree to show David where the Amalekites were?

_____ e. What did David do to the Amalekites when he found them? (See also Bible Dictionary, p. 629, s.v. "Camel.")

_____ f. To whom did David send part of the spoil? (See 1 Samuel 30:31a.)

1 Samuel 31

_____ a. What did the men of Israel do in the battle with the Philistines?

_____ b. What happened to the sons of Saul?

_____ c. How did Saul die?

_____ d. What happened to their bodies?

The Second Book of SAMUEL

2 Samuel 1

_____ a. What did the young Amalekite tell David?

_____ b. Why did David have the young Amalekite killed?

_____ c. For whom did David lament?

2 Samuel 2

_____ a. How did David know that he should go to Hebron?

_____ b. Who went with David to Hebron?

_____ c. What did the men of Judah do when they came to David?

_____ d. What did Abner, "captain of Saul's host" do with Saul's son Ish-bosheth? (2 Samuel 2:8.)

_____ e. How many of David's servants had been killed?

_____ f. How many of the men of Benjamin and Abner were killed?

2 Samuel 3

_____ a. What happened during the long war between the house of Saul and the house of David?

_____ b. How many sons were born to David in Hebron?

_____ c. How did Ish-bosheth offend Abner?

_____ d. What covenant did Abner want to make with David? (See also 2 Samuel 3:12a.)

_____ e. Why did Joab kill Abner? (See also vv. 18–23.)

_____ f. How did David respond to Abner's death?

_____ g. How wise was David?

2 Samuel 4

_____ a. What did the two captains do to Ish-bosheth?

_____ b. How did David reward them? Why?

2 Samuel 5

_____ a. What did all the elders of Israel do to David at Hebron?

_____ b. How old was David when he began to reign?

_____ c. Where did David go after being anointed king over Israel?

_____ d. Who built David a house?

_____ e. Why did David inquire of the Lord?

_____ f. What was David able to do?

_____ g. What did the Lord tell David to do when the Philistines came again?

---

2 Samuel 6

_____ a. Why did David and thirty thousand "chosen men of Israel" go to Gibeah?

_____ b. Why did Uzzah die? (See also D&C 85:8.)

_____ c. Why did David put the ark in the house of Obed-edom the Gittite?

_____ d. Why did David take the ark to the city of David?

_____ e. What did David do when he had finished offering sacrifices?

_____ f. Why was Michal upset with David? (See v. 20a.)

_____ g. What blessing was denied Michal?

---

2 Samuel 7

_____ a. What did David say to Nathan the prophet?

_____ b. What did the Lord tell Nathan to say to David about a house of the Lord?

_____ c. What questions did David ask the Lord?

_____ d. What blessing did David ask of the Lord?

---

2 Samuel 8

_____ a. What did the Lord do for David wherever he went? (See also Map 7.)

_____ b. What did David do with the silver and gold he obtained from all the nations he subdued?

---

2 Samuel 9

_____ a. What did David say to Mephibosheth, Jonathan's son?

_____ b. What did David say to Ziba?

---

2 Samuel 10

_____ a. Why did David send his servants to Hanun, king of the Ammonites? (See also Bible Dictionary, p. 607, s.v. "Ammon, Ammonites.")

_____ b. What did Hanun's servants say to him?

_____ c. What did Hanun do to David's servants?

_____ d. Why did the Ammonites hire the Syrians?

_____ e. What did Joab say to encourage his army? (See also Alma 46:12.)

_____ f. Why did the Syrians fear "to help the children of Ammon any more"? (2 Samuel 10:19.)

---

2 Samuel 11

_____ a. What did David's army do to the children of Ammon? When?

_____ b. What did David do after he saw Bath-sheba washing herself?

_____ c. What did Bath-sheba tell David?

_____ d. What did David tell Uriah to do?

_____ e. What did Uriah do instead? Why?

_____ f. What did David tell Joab to do?

_____ g. How did Uriah die?

_____ h. What happened to Bath-sheba after she had mourned for Uriah?

_____ i. What did the Lord say about what David had done? (See D&C 132:39.)

---

2 Samuel 12

_____ a. Why did Nathan the prophet come to David?

_____ b. How did David react to the parable of the ewe lamb?

_____ c. What did Nathan tell David?

_____ d. What happened to Bath-sheba's child? Why?

_____ e. What was the name of Bath-sheba's next son?

_____ f. Why did David go to the Ammonites?

---

2 Samuel 13

VERSE NUMBER

_____ a. What two great evils did Amnon do to Tamar?

_____ b. What did Tamar do?

_____ c. What did Absalom say of his brother?

_____ d. What happened to Amnon? Why?

---

2 Samuel 14

VERSE NUMBER

_____ a. Why did Joab seek the return of Absalom?

_____ b. What final question did David ask the woman of Tekoah?

_____ c. What did the woman answer?

_____ d. What did David command Joab to do?

_____ e. For how many years had Absalom been away from David? (See 2 Samuel 13:38; 14:28.)

_____ f. What did Absalom do when Joab refused to come to him?

_____ g. What happened when Absalom "came to the king"? (2 Samuel 14:33.)

---

2 Samuel 15

VERSE NUMBER

_____ a. How did Absalom steal the hearts of the children of Israel?

_____ b. What did the messenger say to David?

_____ c. Why did David flee from Jerusalem quickly?

_____ d. What did David tell Zadok to do?

_____ e. What did David tell Hushai to do?

---

2 Samuel 16

_____ a. Who was Ziba? (See 2 Samuel 9:9–12.)

_____ b. What did Ziba tell king David about Jonathan's son Mephibosheth?

_____ c. What did Shimei do when David and his group passed by him?

_____ d. Why did David refuse to let Abishai smite Shimei?

_____ e. Where did Absalom go?

_____ f. What did Ahithophel counsel Absalom to do?

_____ g. Of what value was the counsel of Ahithophel?

---

2 Samuel 17

_____ a. What did Ahithophel counsel Absalom to let him do?

_____ b. What was the counsel of Hushai?

_____ c. How did David know what Absalom was going to do?

_____ d. What did Ahithophel do when Absalom rejected his counsel?

_____ e. Whom did Amasa replace as captain of Absalom's host?

---

2 Samuel 18

_____ a. Why did the people want David not to go with them to battle?

_____ b. What did the king charge his captains concerning Absalom?

_____ c. How did Absalom die?

_____ d. What did David do and say when he heard of Absalom's death?

2 Samuel 19

_____ a. What did Joab tell David to do? Why?

_____ b. Whom did Amasa replace as captain of David's host?

_____ c. What message did the men of Judah send to David?

_____ d. What did David swear to Shimei? (See also 2 Samuel 16:5–13.)

_____ e. How did David deal with Mephibosheth for being disloyal?

_____ f. What did Barzillai do for David? What did David do in return?

2 Samuel 20

_____ a. Who was Sheba? (See also 2 Samuel 16:7a.)

_____ b. Who followed Sheba?

_____ c. What did David do for the concubines he had left in Jerusalem? (See also 2 Samuel 16:21–22; Deuteronomy 24:1–4.)

_____ d. What happened to Amasa, David's captain?

_____ e. What did the wise woman of Abel do?

2 Samuel 21

_____ a. Why was there a famine in the land? (See also Joshua 9:3–17.)

_____ b. What did the Gibeonites ask of David?

_____ c. What did the Gibeonites do with the sons of Saul?

_____ d. List four men whom David and his servants slew.

2 Samuel 22

_____ a. How did David praise the Lord? (See also Bible Dictionary, p. 653, s.v. "David.")

_____ b. What is the Lord to David? Why?

---

2 Samuel 23

_____ a. By what power did David speak?

_____ b. What must rulers do?

_____ c. Whose deeds did David extol?

_____ d. What did Adino the Eznite do?

_____ e. What did Abishai do?

---

2 Samuel 24

_____ a. What did David command Joab to do? Why?

_____ b. How many men were in Israel? in Judah?

_____ c. How had David sinned?

_____ d. What did the Lord instruct the prophet Gad to tell David?

_____ e. List the three judgments that the Lord allowed David to choose from.

_____ f. Why did the angel refrain from destroying Jerusalem? (See 2 Samuel 24:16a.)

_____ g. What did David do to stop the plague?

The First Book of the KINGS

Introduction

See Bible Dictionary, page 721, s.v. "Kings, Books of."

_____ a. What history is contained in the books of Kings?

_____ b. Where is the "succession of events" found? (See Bible Dictionary, p. 635, s.v. "Chronology.")

_____ c. What sources were used to compile the books of Kings?

---

1 Kings 1

_____ a. Who was Adonijah?

_____ b. Why did Bath-sheba go to David?

_____ c. What did David swear to Bath-sheba?

_____ d. What did David command be done with Solomon?

_____ e. What news did Jonathan give to Adonijah?

_____ f. What did the guests of Adonijah do? Why?

_____ g. What did Solomon say about Adonijah?

---

1 Kings 2

_____ a. What did David charge Solomon to do?

_____ b. What was required if the kings of Israel were to be descendants of David?

_____ c. List three things David charged Solomon to do after his death.

_____ d. What happened to Adonijah? Why?

_____ e. What happened to Abiathar? Why? (See also 1 Kings 1:18–19.)

_____ f. What happened to Joab? Why? (See also 2 Samuel 18:10–17.)

_____ g. What happened to Shimei? Why? (See also 2 Samuel 16:5–13.)

---

1 Kings 3

_____ a. What did the Lord say when he appeared to Solomon in a dream?

_____ b. What did Solomon desire?

_____ c. What did the Lord do for Solomon? Why?

_____ d. What was required of Solomon for him to have a long life?

_____ e. How did Solomon determine who was the mother of the living child?

---

1 Kings 4

_____ a. Who "brought presents, and served Solomon all the days of his life"? (1 Kings 4:21; see also Map 8.)

_____ b. What had God given to Solomon?

_____ c. Why did the "kings of the earth" visit Solomon? (V. 34.)

---

1 Kings 5

_____ a. Who sent his servants to Solomon?

_____ b. What could David not do?

_____ c. What did Solomon propose to do?

_____ d. Why did Solomon desire to hire the servants of Hiram?

_____ e. What did Hiram do when he "heard the words of Solomon"? (1 Kings 5:7.)

_____ f. What did Solomon and Hiram make together? (See v. 12b.)

_____ g. About how many men did Solomon employ? (See also v. 15b.)

---

1 Kings 6

_____ a. List three items that were used to build the temple.

_____ b. What did the Lord require Solomon to do?

_____ c. How many years did it take Solomon to build the temple?

---

1 Kings 7

_____ a. How long did it take Solomon to build his house?

_____ b. What other houses did Solomon build?

_____ c. Why did Solomon hire Hiram the brassworker? (See also Bible Dictionary, p. 703, s.v. "Hiram.")

_____ d. What was the "molten sea"? (1 Kings 7:23.)

_____ e. What did the molten sea rest upon?

_____ f. List seven things Hiram cast "in the clay ground." (V. 46.)

_____ g. List five things Solomon had made of pure gold.

_____ h. What did Solomon put "among the treasures of the house of the Lord"? (V. 51.)

---

1 Kings 8

VERSE NUMBER

_____ a. Whom did Solomon assemble? Why?

_____ b. What was in the ark?

_____ c. Why were the priests unable to minister?

_____ d. What is recorded in verses 12 through 53?

_____ e. What did Solomon ask the Lord to hearken to?

_____ f. What did Solomon ask the Lord to do for any man who prayed toward the temple? the people when there was no rain because of sin? any man who prayed for help? the stranger who came and prayed to the Lord? the people who went to battle? the people who were carried away captive and repent?

_____ g. Why did Israel want the Lord to be with them?

_____ h. What were the people to let their hearts become?

_____ i. What did the people do after the temple dedication and the feast?

1 Kings 9

_____ a. When did the Lord appear to Solomon a second time? (See also 1 Kings 3:5.)

_____ b. What was Solomon to do in order for the Lord to "establish the throne of [his] kingdom upon Israel for ever"? (1 Kings 9:5.)

_____ c. What would the Lord do if Solomon did not follow Him?

_____ d. What did Solomon give to Hiram, king of Tyre, for his help?

_____ e. How was Solomon's gift received by Hiram? (See v. 13a.)

_____ f. Who were Solomon's bondsmen?

_____ g. What positions did the children of Israel hold?

_____ h. How did Hiram help Solomon?

1 Kings 10

_____ a. Why did the queen of Sheba visit Solomon?

_____ b. What did the queen tell Solomon?

_____ c. What did Solomon tell the queen?

_____ d. How impressed was the queen with Solomon?

_____ e. What did Solomon give the queen?

_____ f. How did Solomon exceed all the kings of the earth?

1 Kings 11

_____ a. How did the wives of Solomon turn away his heart? (See also D&C 132:38.)

_____ b. Why was the Lord angry with Solomon?

_____ c. What did the Lord tell Solomon he would do? When?

_____ d. Who was Hadad?

_____ e. Why did Solomon make Jeroboam ruler "over all the charge of the house of Joseph"? (1 Kings 11:28.)

_____ f. Why could the Lord not forgive Solomon? (See v. 33c.)

_____ g. What did the prophet Ahijah tell Jeroboam about his future? (See v. 38b.)

_____ h. Why did Jeroboam flee to Egypt?

---

1 Kings 12

VERSE NUMBER

_____ a. Why had all Israel gone to Shechem?

_____ b. Upon what condition would Jeroboam and all Israel serve Rehoboam?

_____ c. What counsel did the elders give Rehoboam?

_____ d. What counsel did the young men give Rehoboam? (See also 1 Kings 12:11b.)

_____ e. Why did Israel rebel against Rehoboam? (See also Map 9; Bible Dictionary, p. 708, s.v. "Israel, kingdom of.")

_____ f. Whom did Israel make their king?

_____ g. Which tribe followed Rehoboam?

_____ h. Why did Rehoboam refrain from fighting against the house of Israel?

_____ i. What did Jeroboam do to anger the Lord? Why?

---

1 Kings 13

VERSE NUMBER

_____ a. What did the prophet prophesy would happen on the altar?

_____ b. What sign did the prophet give that this event would happen?

_____ c. What happened to Jeroboam when he ordered his servants to seize the prophet?

_____ d. How was Jeroboam healed?

_____ e. What happened to the prophet after he came back? Why?

_____ f. What was to happen to the house of Jeroboam because of his evil ways?

1 Kings 14

_____ a. Why did Jeroboam send his wife and son to Ahijah the prophet?

_____ b. What did Ahijah say would happen to Jeroboam's house? Why?

_____ c. What would the Lord do to Israel? Why?

_____ d. Where were the acts of Jeroboam recorded? (See also 1 Kings 14:19a.)

_____ e. Who replaced Jeroboam as king of Israel?

_____ f. What did Judah do to anger the Lord? (See also v. 24a.)

_____ g. What did Shishak, king of Egypt, do in the fifth year of Rehoboam's reign?

_____ h. Who replaced Rehoboam on the throne?

1 Kings 15

_____ a. How did Abijam follow his father?

_____ b. What did Asa do as king of Judah "which was right in the eyes of the Lord"? (1 Kings 15:11.)

_____ c. Who fought against each other all their days?

_____ d. Who replaced Asa as king of Judah?

_____ e. How did Nadab, king of Israel and son of Jeroboam, anger the Lord?

_____ f. What happened to Nadab?

_____ g. What did Baasha do to the house of Jeroboam?

_____ h. What did Baasha do as king of Israel "in the sight of the Lord"? (V. 34.)

1 Kings 16

_____ a. What did Jehu prophesy would happen to Baasha? Why?

_____ b. Who replaced Baasha as king of Israel?

_____ c. How and by whom was Elah, king of Israel, replaced?

_____ d. What did Zimri do as soon as he became king of Israel?

_____ e. What did Zimri do when the people made Omri king?

_____ f. How were the people of Israel divided?

_____ g. What did Omri do in the sight of the Lord?

_____ h. What did Ahab, Omri's son, do in the sight of the Lord?

---

1 Kings 17

_____ a. What did Elijah say to Ahab, king of Israel?

_____ b. What did the ravens do for Elijah?

_____ c. What did Elijah ask the widow to do?

_____ d. What did Elijah tell her about the barrel of meal and the cruse of oil?

_____ e. How was the widow's son raised from the dead?

---

1 Kings 18

_____ a. To whom did the Lord send Elijah?

_____ b. How had Obadiah saved the prophets from Jezebel?

_____ c. What did Ahab say to Elijah about the drought?

_____ d. What was Elijah's response?

_____ e. What did Elijah tell Ahab to do?

_____ f. Whom did Elijah challenge the people to follow?

_____ g. What did Elijah say to the Lord to cause the fire to fall?

_____ h. What did the fire do?

_____ i. What did the people do when they saw the fire?

_____ j. What happened to the priests of Baal?

---

1 Kings 19

VERSE NUMBER

_____ a. What message did Jezebel send to Elijah?

_____ b. How did Elijah respond?

_____ c. What did Elijah do for forty days and forty nights on Mount Horeb? (See 1 Kings 19:8a; see also Bible Dictionary, p. 664, s.v. "Elijah.")

_____ d. What did Elijah tell the Lord?

_____ e. How did the Lord speak to Elijah?

_____ f. List three things the Lord commanded Elijah to do.

_____ g. How many Israelites had not worshiped Baal?

---

1 Kings 20

VERSE NUMBER

_____ a. What request of Ben-hadad did Ahab refuse?

_____ b. What message from the Lord did a prophet deliver to Ahab?

_____ c. What did Israel do to the Syrians?

_____ d. What message from the Lord was given to Ahab before the second fight?

_____ e. How did Ahab show mercy to Ben-hadad?

_____ f. How did Ahab incur the anger of the Lord?

---

1 Kings 21

VERSE NUMBER

_____ a. Why did Naboth refuse to sell his vineyard to Ahab?

_____ b. How did Jezebel obtain the vineyard for Ahab?

_____ c. What did Elijah tell Ahab would happen to him and Jezebel? Why?

_____ d. What did Ahab do when he heard this message? (See also 1 Kings 21:27b.)

_____ e. What did the Lord tell Elijah?

---

1 Kings 22

_____ a. With whom did the king of Israel and the king of Judah desire to fight? Why?

_____ b. What did the prophets of Ahab prophesy?

_____ c. What did Micaiah prophesy?

_____ d. What did the king of Syria command his captains of chariots to do?

_____ e. What happened to Ahab?

_____ f. What did Jehoshaphat, king of Judah, do "in the eyes of the Lord"? (1 Kings 22:43.)

_____ g. What did Ahaziah, son of Ahab, do "in the sight of the Lord"? (V. 52.)

The Second Book of the KINGS

---

2 Kings 1

VERSE NUMBER

_____ a. What message did Elijah deliver to the king's servants?

_____ b. What happened when the captain and his fifty went to get Elijah?

_____ c. What happened when the second captain and his fifty went to get Elijah?

_____ d. What happened when the third captain and his fifty went to get Elijah?

_____ e. Why was Ahaziah, the king of Israel, to die?

_____ f. Who replaced Ahaziah as king of Israel?

---

2 Kings 2

VERSE NUMBER

_____ a. What did Elisha ask of Elijah?

_____ b. How would Elisha know if his request would be granted?

_____ c. How was Elijah taken away?

_____ d. How was Elisha received by the sons of the prophets?

_____ e. What did Elisha do to the waters at Jericho?

_____ f. What happened to those who mocked Elisha the prophet? (See 2 Kings 2:23a.)

---

2 Kings 3

VERSE NUMBER

_____ a. What did Jehoram, king of Israel, do in the sight of the Lord?

_____ b. What did he ask Jehoshaphat to help him do? Why?

_____ c. With whom did Jehoshaphat want to speak? Why?

_____ d. What was the message of the Lord?

_____ e. What did the king of Moab do to his eldest son?

---

2 Kings 4

VERSE NUMBER

_____ a. How did Elisha help the widow pay her debts?

_____ b. What did the Shunammite woman do for Elisha?

_____ c. How was she rewarded for her service?

_____ d. How was her son healed?

_____ e. What did Elisha do to the deadly pottage?

---

2 Kings 5

VERSE NUMBER

_____ a. List six things we learn about Naaman.

_____ b. Why did Naaman go to Israel?

_____ c. What message did Elisha send to the king of Israel?

_____ d. What message did Elisha send to Naaman?

_____ e. How did Naaman react? Why?

_____ f. What happened to Naaman when he washed in the River Jordan?

_____ g. What did Gehazi do after Naaman left Elisha?

_____ h. What happened to Gehazi?

2 Kings 6

_____ a. What message did Elisha send to the king of Israel?

_____ b. What did Elisha say when his servant saw the Syrian army?

_____ c. What happened to the Syrian army that came for Elisha?

_____ d. What did Elisha tell the king of Israel to do to the army?

_____ e. What was the result of feeding the Syrians and letting them go?

2 Kings 7

_____ a. What did Elisha prophesy would happen?

_____ b. Why did the Syrians flee?

_____ c. What did they leave behind?

_____ d. How was Elisha's prophecy fulfilled?

2 Kings 8

_____ a. Why did Elisha tell the Shunammite woman to leave?

_____ b. What did the king grant her upon her return?

_____ c. What did Hazael deliver to Elisha as a present from Ben-hadad, king of Syria?

_____ d. What message did Elisha give Hazael?

_____ e. Why did Elisha weep?

_____ f. How did Ben-hadad die?

_____ g. Who reigned in Judah after Jehoshaphat?

_____ h. What did Jehoram, king of Judah, do "in the sight of the Lord"? (2 Kings 8:18.)

_____ i. Why did Ahaziah, king of Judah, do evil "in the sight of the Lord"? (V. 27.)

2 Kings 9

_____ a. What did Elisha send "one of the children of the prophets" to do? (2 Kings 9:1.)

_____ b. What did the messenger tell Jehu?

_____ c. What did Jehu do to Jehoram, king of Israel?

_____ d. What happened to Ahaziah, king of Judah?

_____ e. What happened to Jezebel?

2 Kings 10

_____ a. What did Jehu require of the leaders of Samaria in the second letter?

_____ b. What did Jehu do to the house of Ahab?

_____ c. Why did Jehu gather the followers of Baal together?

_____ d. What evil did Jehu fail to destroy?

_____ e. Who replaced Jehu as king of Israel?

2 Kings 11

_____ a. What did Athaliah do when she learned that her son Ahaziah was dead?

_____ b. What did Jehoiada the priest command the rulers and captains to do?

_____ c. What happened to Athaliah?

_____ d. What covenant did Jehoiada make?

_____ e. What happened to the house of Baal?

_____ f. How old was Joash when he began to reign over Judah? (See also Bible Dictionary, p. 638, s.v. "Chronology.")

---

2 Kings 12

_____ a. What did Joash do "in the sight of the Lord"? (See also Bible Dictionary, p. 713, s.v. "Joash (3).")

_____ b. What did Joash ask the priests to repair? (See also 2 Kings 12:6a.)

_____ c. Why did Hazael, king of Syria, depart from Jerusalem?

_____ d. What happened to Joash?

_____ e. Who reigned in his stead?

---

2 Kings 13

_____ a. What did Jehoahaz, king of Israel and son of Jehu, do "in the sight of the Lord"? (2 Kings 13:2.)

_____ b. Into whose hands was Israel delivered?

_____ c. What did Jehoash, king of Israel, do "in the sight of the Lord"? (V. 11.)

_____ d. Who replaced Jehoash as king of Israel?

_____ e. Who visited Elisha when he was sick?

_____ f. What did Elisha prophesy to Jehoash, king of Israel?

---

2 Kings 14

_____ a. What did Amaziah do "in the sight of the Lord"? (2 Kings 14:3.)

_____ b. What did Amaziah do to those who had slain his father? (See also 2 Kings 12:20–21.)

_____ c. What did Amaziah, king of Judah, and Jehoash, king of Israel, do when they met?

_____ d. What did Jehoash do at Jerusalem?

_____ e. Who replaced Jehoash as king of Israel?

_____ f. What happened to Amaziah?

_____ g. Who replaced Amaziah as king of Judah?

_____ h. Who replaced Jeroboam as king of Israel?

2 Kings 15

_____ a. Who replaced Amaziah as king of Judah?

_____ b. What did Azariah, king of Judah, do "in the sight of the Lord"? (2 Kings 15:3.)

_____ c. What did the Lord do to Azariah?

_____ d. Who replaced Azariah as king of Judah?

_____ e. What did Zachariah, king of Israel, do "in the sight of the Lord"? (V. 9.)

_____ f. Who replaced Zachariah as king of Israel?

_____ g. Who took much of Israel captive in the days of Pekah? (See v. 29; see also Bible Dictionary, p. 615, s.v. "Assyria"; Map 10.)

2 Kings 16

_____ a. What did Ahaz do "in the sight of the Lord"? (2 Kings 16:2.)

_____ b. Why did Ahaz send gold and silver to the king of Assyria?

_____ c. What did Ahaz have built that was like the Assyrians had?

_____ d. What did Ahaz take off the brazen oxen? (See headnote to 1 Kings 7.)

2 Kings 17

_____ a. Why did the king of Assyria put Hoshea in prison?

_____ b. What did the king of Assyria do to Israel?

_____ c. How had Israel offended the Lord?

_____ d. What happened to Israel? (See also D&C 132:26–35.)

_____ e. What did the Lord do to some Assyrians who lived in the cities of Israel? Why?

_____ f. What had the Israelites covenanted with the Lord?

2 Kings 18

_____ a. What did Hezekiah do "in the sight of the Lord"? (2 Kings 18:3.)

_____ b. Why did he break the brazen serpent that Moses had made?

_____ c. In whom did Hezekiah trust?

_____ d. Which commandments did he keep?

_____ e. What did Rabshakeh tell the people of Judah, in their own language, to do?

_____ f. Why did the people not answer him?

2 Kings 19

_____ a. To whom did Hezekiah send his servants?

_____ b. What did Isaiah say to the servants?

_____ c. What message did the Assyrians send to Hezekiah?

_____ d. What did Hezekiah ask of the Lord?

_____ e. What message did Isaiah send to Hezekiah?

_____ f. What happened to the Assyrian army?

_____ g. What happened to the king of Assyria?

2 Kings 20

_____ a. What did Hezekiah say to the Lord when Isaiah told him he would die?

_____ b. What message did the Lord give Isaiah for Hezekiah?

_____ c. What sign was given Hezekiah that he would be healed?

_____ d. What was the Lord's message that Isaiah gave Hezekiah after he had shown the Babylonians all his treasure? (See also Bible Dictionary, p. 618, s.v. "Babylon.")

_____ e. What did Hezekiah bring into the city? How?

---

2 Kings 21

_____ a. What did Manasseh do "in the sight of the Lord"? (2 Kings 21:2.)

_____ b. How much evil did Manasseh cause the people to commit?

_____ c. What did the Lord say through his prophets?

_____ d. What did Amon, the son of Manasseh, do "in the sight of the Lord"? (V. 20.)

_____ e. What happened to Amon?

---

2 Kings 22

_____ a. What did Josiah do "in the sight of the Lord"? How? (2 Kings 22:2.)

_____ b. What did Josiah send Shaphan to say to Hilkiah?

_____ c. Why was there no reckoning made of the money?

_____ d. What did Hilkiah give to Shaphan?

_____ e. Upon hearing the contents of the book, what did Josiah say?

_____ f. What did the prophetess say to the king's servants about Jerusalem's future?

_____ g. Why would Josiah not see the evil that would befall Judah?

---

2 Kings 23

_____ a. What did the king read to all the people of Judah and Jerusalem?

_____ b. What did the king and the elders covenant to do?

_____ c. How did Josiah remove idolatry from the land?

_____ d. What happened to the priests of the high places?

_____ e. What did Josiah command the people to observe?

_____ f. Why was no king like Josiah?

_____ g. What happened to Josiah?

_____ h. What did Jehoahaz do "in the sight of the Lord"? (2 Kings 23:32.)

_____ i. What happened to Jehoahaz?

_____ j. What did Jehoiakim do "in the sight of the Lord"? (V. 37.)

---

2 Kings 24

VERSE NUMBER

_____ a. Why did the Lord want "to remove [Judah] out of his sight"? (2 Kings 24:3; see also 21:11.)

_____ b. What did Jehoiachin do "in the sight of the Lord"? (V. 9.)

_____ c. What did Nebuchadnezzar take from Jerusalem? (See also Map 11.)

_____ d. Whom did Nebuchadnezzar make king? (See also 1 Nephi 1:4.)

_____ e. What did Zedekiah do "in the sight of the Lord"? (V. 19.)

---

2 Kings 25

VERSE NUMBER

_____ a. Why did Nebuchadnezzer march against Jerusalem? (See 2 Kings 24:20.)

_____ b. What did the men of war in Jerusalem do?

_____ c. What happened to Zedekiah?

_____ d. What did the captain of the guard of Babylon do in Jerusalem?

_____ e. What did the king of Babylon do to the captives brought to him by the captain of the guard?

_____ f. Who was made ruler of the people in the land of Judah?

_____ g. Why did the people flee to Egypt?

_____ h. What did the king of Babylon do for Jehoiachin?

The First Book of the CHRONICLES

Introduction

See Bible Dictionary, page 635, s.v. "Chronicles."

_____ a. What period of history is covered by the two books of Chronicles?

_____ b. What do references in Chronicles to other books help us to understand?

_____ c. How did the compilers choose what to include in Chronicles?

_____ d. What did these compilers dwell upon?

_____ e. What two books may be regarded as a sequel to 1 and 2 Chronicles?

---

1 Chronicles 1

VERSE NUMBER

_____ a. Whose genealogies and family ties are listed in 1 Chronicles 1? (See also Bible Dictionary, p. 678, s.v. "Genealogy.")

_____ b. Whose posterity is listed in chapter 1?

_____ c. What happened in the days of Peleg? (See also D&C 133:24.)

---

1 Chronicles 2

VERSE NUMBER

_____ a. Whose posterities are named in 1 Chronicles 2?

---

1 Chronicles 3

VERSE NUMBER

_____ a. Whose sons are named in 1 Chronicles 3?

_____ b. Which successors of Solomon are listed?

---

1 Chronicles 4

VERSE NUMBER

_____ a. Whose families and descendants are chronicled in 1 Chronicles 4?

b. Who else is named?

c. What did God grant to Jabez?

---

1 Chronicles 5

_____ a. Who received Reuben's birthright? Why?

_____ b. Who did the Assyrians carry into captivity? Why?

---

1 Chronicles 6

_____ a. Whose sons are listed in 1 Chronicles 6?

_____ b. What did Aaron and his sons do?

---

1 Chronicles 7

_____ a. Whose sons and families are named in 1 Chronicles 7?

---

1 Chronicles 8

_____ a. Whose sons and chief men are named in 1 Chronicles 8?

---

1 Chronicles 9

_____ a. How were the people of Israel reckoned?

_____ b. The inhabitants of which city are listed in 1 Chronicles 9?

_____ c. Whose family is named?

---

1 Chronicles 10

_____ a. What happened to the sons of Saul in the battle with the Philistines?

_____ b. What did Saul do after being wounded?

_____ c. What did the men of Israel do?

_____ d. What did the Philistines do with Saul?

_____ e. What did the valiant men of Jabesh-gilead do?

_____ f. Why did Saul die? (See also 1 Samuel 13:9–14; 15:17–23; 28:6–8.)

---

1 Chronicles 11

VERSE NUMBER

_____ a. What did the elders of Israel do after David made a covenant with them?

_____ b. How was David able to "[wax] greater and greater"? (1 Chronicles 11:9.)

_____ c. What did Jashobeam do?

_____ d. What did the three mighty men do when David was thirsty?

---

1 Chronicles 12

VERSE NUMBER

_____ a. Whose mighty men are listed?

_____ b. Who joined David at Hebron?

_____ c. Who rejoiced in King David?

---

1 Chronicles 13

VERSE NUMBER

_____ a. What did David propose to Israel?

_____ b. Why did the Lord smite Uzza?

_____ c. Why did David leave the ark in the house of Obed-edom?

_____ d. What did the Lord do to the house of Obed-edom while the ark of God was there?

---

1 Chronicles 14

VERSE NUMBER

_____ a. What did David do at Jerusalem? (See also D&C 132:38–39.)

113

_____ b. What did David do when the Philistines came? when they came again?

---

1 Chronicles 15

_____ a. Why did David tell the Levites to sanctify themselves?

_____ b. How did Israel bring the ark into Jerusalem?

_____ c. Why did Michal despise David? (See 2 Samuel 6:20c.)

---

1 Chronicles 16

_____ a. What did David do when he finished his offerings?

_____ b. What did David deliver into the hand of Asaph and his brethren?

_____ c. What counsel did David give in his psalm?

_____ d. What were Asaph and his brethren to do?

---

1 Chronicles 17

_____ a. What did David desire to do?

_____ b. What did the Lord say to Nathan the prophet?

_____ c. What did David ask of the Lord?

---

1 Chronicles 18

_____ a. How was David able to smite all the adversaries of Israel?

_____ b. What did David do with the silver and gold he acquired?

_____ c. What did David do as he reigned over all Israel?

---

1 Chronicles 19

_____ a. How did Hanun, king of the Ammonites, treat David's servants? Why?

_____ b. How did the king seek to protect himself from David?

_____ c. What did Joab say to his brother Abishai?

_____ d. What did the Syrians and the Ammonites do?

_____ e. What did David do to the Syrians when they came again?

---

1 Chronicles 20

_____ a. What did David and Joab do to the Ammonites and their cities?

_____ b. Whom did Elhanan slay?

_____ c. Whom did Jonathan slay?

---

1 Chronicles 21

_____ a. How did David sin against the Lord?

_____ b. How many men were in Israel?

_____ c. How many men were in Judah?

_____ d. What three punishments were given David to choose from?

_____ e. Which one did David choose?

_____ f. How many men died?

_____ g. What did David build on the threshing floor where the angel stopped?

---

1 Chronicles 22

_____ a. What did David do to prepare for building the temple? Why?

_____ b. What did David charge his son Solomon to do?

_____ c. Why did David not build the temple?

_____ d. What was required of Solomon for him to prosper?

_____ e. What did David say to the princes of Israel?

1 Chronicles 23

VERSE NUMBER

_____ a. Whom did David make king over Israel?

_____ b. What were the Levites assigned to do?

1 Chronicles 24

VERSE NUMBER

_____ a. Who were divided into groups? (See also Bible Dictionary, p. 599, s.v. "Aaronic Priesthood.")

_____ b. How were they assigned their duties?

1 Chronicles 25

VERSE NUMBER

_____ a. In 1 Chronicles 25 who were assigned duties?

1 Chronicles 26

VERSE NUMBER

_____ a. Who were assigned to be porters?

_____ b. List three duties they had.

1 Chronicles 27

VERSE NUMBER

_____ a. What two groups are named in 1 Chronicles 27?

1 Chronicles 28

VERSE NUMBER

_____ a. What five things did David tell those he assembled at Jerusalem?

_____ b. What counsel did David give to Solomon?

_____ c. What did David give to Solomon?

---

1 Chronicles 29

_____ a. How had David prepared for the house of the Lord?

_____ b. What did David ask of the congregation?

_____ c. How did the leaders respond?

_____ d. List six things we learn from David's prayer to the Lord.

_____ e. How did the Lord magnify Solomon in the sight of all Israel?

The Second Book of the CHRONICLES

---

2 Chronicles 1

_____ a. What did the Lord say to Solomon after he had offered burnt offerings?

_____ b. What did Solomon ask of the Lord?

_____ c. What did the Lord say to Solomon?

---

2 Chronicles 2

_____ a. How many men did Solomon employ to obtain stones? (See also 2 Chronicles 2:2a.)

_____ b. What did Solomon ask of Huram, king of Tyre?

_____ c. What did Huram answer?

---

2 Chronicles 3

_____ a. Where did Solomon build the temple?

_____ b. What metal did Solomon use much of in building the temple?

---

2 Chronicles 4

_____ a. What did Solomon place upon the twelve oxen?

_____ b. What were the temple doors made of?

---

2 Chronicles 5

_____ a. What did "the priests and the Levites bring up" to the temple? (2 Chronicles 5:5.)

_____ b. What was in the ark?

_____ c. What did the singers sing?

_____ d. Why were the priests unable to minister?

---

2 Chronicles 6

_____ a. Whom did Solomon bless?

_____ b. What promise had the Lord fulfilled when the temple was built?

_____ c. List six things Solomon asked in his prayer in verses 14 through 42.

---

2 Chronicles 7

_____ a. What happened when Solomon finished praying?

_____ b. What did the people do when they saw it?

_____ c. How long did the feast last?

_____ d. What did Solomon do with what came into his heart for the house of the Lord?

_____ e. What did the Lord tell Solomon when He appeared to him?

_____ f. Under what conditions would the Lord destroy his temple?

---

2 Chronicles 8

_____ a. How long was Solomon building the temple and his house?

_____ b. What did Solomon require of the people in the land who were not of Israel?

_____ c. What did the men of Israel do?

_____ d. Whom did Solomon appoint according to the order established by David? What were they to do?

---

2 Chronicles 9

_____ a. Why did the queen of Sheba visit Solomon?

_____ b. What did Solomon tell the queen?

_____ c. What did the queen say to Solomon?

_____ d. What did she give to Solomon?

_____ e. What did Solomon give to the queen of Sheba?

_____ f. How was Solomon greater than all other kings of the earth?

_____ g. Why did all the kings seek the presence of Solomon?

_____ h. What lost books are named in 2 Chronicles 9? (See also v. 29a.)

---

2 Chronicles 10

_____ a. Why did all Israel go to Shechem?

_____ b. What did Jeroboam and all of Israel say to Rehoboam?

_____ c. What counsel did the old men give to Rehoboam?

_____ d. What counsel did the young men give to Rehoboam?

_____ e. Why did Israel rebel against the house of David?

2 Chronicles 11

_____ a. What did the Lord say to Shemaiah?

_____ b. Why did all the priests and Levites go to Judah?

_____ c. What did Jeroboam do in Israel?

2 Chronicles 12

_____ a. What did Rehoboam and all of Israel forsake?

_____ b. Why did Shishak, king of Egypt, go against Jerusalem?

_____ c. Why did the Lord refrain from destroying Jerusalem?

_____ d. What did Shishak take from Jerusalem?

_____ e. How did Rehoboam do evil?

_____ f. What lost books are named in 2 Chronicles 12? (See also v. 15a.)

2 Chronicles 13

_____ a. Who replaced Rehoboam as king of Judah?

_____ b. What did Abijah say to Jeroboam and Israel before the battle?

_____ c. What did the men of Judah do when they were ambushed?

_____ d. Why did Israel flee before Judah?

2 Chronicles 14

_____ a. What did Asa, king of Judah, do "in the eyes of the Lord"? (2 Chronicles 14:2.)

_____ b. Why did a million Ethiopians flee before Asa?

_____ c. What did Asa take back to Jerusalem?

2 Chronicles 15

_____ a. What was the Lord's message that Azariah gave to Asa?

_____ b. What did Asa do when he heard this message?

_____ c. Why did people from other tribes flee to Asa?

_____ d. What covenant did the people make with the Lord?

_____ e. How did the Lord bless them?

2 Chronicles 16

VERSE NUMBER

_____ a. How did Asa defeat Israel?

_____ b. Why had the host of Syria escaped from Asa?

_____ c. What does the Lord do for those whose heart is perfect toward him?

_____ d. How had Asa done foolishly?

_____ e. Whom did Asa seek in his sickness?

2 Chronicles 17

VERSE NUMBER

_____ a. Why was the Lord with Jehoshaphat?

_____ b. Why did he send his servants to the cities of Judah?

_____ c. What did they teach?

_____ d. Why did Judah's neighbors refrain from making war against Judah?

2 Chronicles 18

VERSE NUMBER

_____ a. How did Jehoshaphat have "affinity" with Ahab? (See 2 Chronicles 18:1a.)

_____ b. What did Jehoshaphat ask Ahab to do before going to war against the Syrians?

_____ c. What did Ahab's prophets counsel them to do?

_____ d. What did Micaiah say to Ahab?

_____ e. What did Ahab command be done with Micaiah?

_____ f. How was Jehoshaphat able to escape?

_____ g. What happened to Ahab?

---

2 Chronicles 19

_____ a. Why was the wrath of the Lord upon Jehoshaphat?

_____ b. What good things had Jehoshaphat done? (See also 2 Chronicles 19:4a.)

_____ c. What did Jehoshaphat tell the judges to do? the priests, Levites, and the "chief of the fathers of Israel" in Jerusalem to do? (V. 8.)

---

2 Chronicles 20

_____ a. Who went against Jehoshaphat to battle?

_____ b. What did Jehoshaphat do?

_____ c. What did Jehoshaphat pray for?

_____ d. What did Jahaziel say to the congregation?

_____ e. What happened to those who went against Judah? (See also 2 Chronicles 20:22a.)

_____ f. How long did it take Judah to gather the spoil?

_____ g. Why were the "high places" not taken away? (V. 33.)

_____ h. Why were the ships "broken"? (V. 37.)

---

2 Chronicles 21

_____ a. What did Jehoram, king of Judah, do to his brothers? (See also Bible Dictionary, p. 710, s.v. "Jehoram or Joram (2).")

_____ b. What did Jehoram do "in the eyes of the Lord"? (2 Chronicles 21:6.) Why?

_____ c. Why did the Lord not destroy Jehoram right away?

_____ d. What wickedness did Jehoram commit? (See also v. 11a.)

_____ e. What did Elijah write to Jehoram?

_____ f. What happened to Jehoram?

2 Chronicles 22

_____ a. Why was Ahaziah made king?

_____ b. Who counseled him to do wickedly? (See also 2 Chronicles 21:6.)

_____ c. What had God appointed Jehu to do?

_____ d. What happened to Ahaziah? Why?

_____ e. What did Athaliah do when her son Ahaziah was killed?

_____ f. How was the house of David preserved?

2 Chronicles 23

_____ a. Who was Jehoiada? (See 2 Chronicles 22:11.)

_____ b. How did Jehoiada arrange for Joash to be crowned king?

_____ c. What did he command be done to the wicked queen?

_____ d. What covenant did Jehoiada, the people, and the king make?

_____ e. What did the people do at the "house of Baal"? (2 Chronicles 23:17.)

_____ f. What did Jehoiada appoint the priests of the Levites to do?

2 Chronicles 24

_____ a. Why did Joash set a collection chest by the temple gate?

_____ b. How were the donations used?

_____ c. How old was Jehoiada the priest when he died?

_____ d. Why was Jehoiada buried with the kings?

_____ e. Whose counsel did Joash take after the death of Jehoiada?

_____ f. Why did the wrath of the Lord come upon Judah and Jerusalem?

_____ g. What did the Lord do to encourage the people of Judah to return to him?

_____ h. What happened to Zechariah, son of Jehoiada, when he testified to the people in the name of God?

_____ i. What happened to Judah and Jerusalem at the end of the year?

_____ j. What happened to Joash? (See also 2 Chronicles 24:25a.)

---

2 Chronicles 25

_____ a. What did Amaziah do "in the sight of the Lord"? (See 2 Chronicles 25:2a.)

_____ b. What did Amaziah do to those who had killed his father?

_____ c. What did the man of God say to Amaziah?

_____ d. Why was the Lord angry with Amaziah?

_____ e. What did the prophet say to Amaziah?

_____ f. What did Joash, king of Israel, do to Jerusalem?

_____ g. What happened to Amaziah?

---

2 Chronicles 26

_____ a. How was Uzziah able to prosper?

_____ b. How did Uzziah prepare his people for war?

_____ c. What sin did Uzziah commmit "when he was strong"? (2 Chronicles 26:16.) Why?

_____ d. What happened to Uzziah?

2 Chronicles 27

VERSE NUMBER

_____ a. What did Jotham do "in the sight of the Lord"? (2 Chronicles 27:2.)

_____ b. How did Jotham become mighty? (See v. 6a.)

2 Chronicles 28

VERSE NUMBER

_____ a. What did Ahaz do "in the sight of the Lord"? (2 Chronicles 28:1.)

_____ b. Why did the Lord deliver Ahaz "into the hand of the king of Syria"? (V. 5.)

_____ c. How was Pekah able to slay one hundred twenty thousand valiant men of Judah in one day?

_____ d. What did the children of Israel do to Judah?

_____ e. Why did Israel free the captives of Judah?

_____ f. How did Ahaz offend the Lord even further?

2 Chronicles 29

VERSE NUMBER

_____ a. What did Hezekiah do "in the sight of the Lord"? (2 Chronicles 29:2.)

_____ b. What did Hezekiah say to the priests and Levites?

_____ c. What did the Levites and priests do to the temple?

_____ d. What did the priests do after the temple was sanctified?

_____ e. Why did Hezekiah and all the people rejoice?

2 Chronicles 30

VERSE NUMBER

_____ a. What message did Hezekiah command be sent to all Israel and Judah?

_____ b. What blessing would the people obtain by turning to the Lord?

_____ c. Why did the Lord heal those who were unclean and yet ate the passover?

_____ d. When was the last time there had been so much joy in Jerusalem?

_____ e. What did the priests and the Levites do?

---

2 Chronicles 31

_____ a. What did "all Israel that were present" do when the feast had ended? (2 Chronicles 31:1.)

_____ b. What did Hezekiah appoint the priests and Levites to do?

_____ c. Why did the people take in their tithes?

_____ d. How did Hezekiah serve God?

---

2 Chronicles 32

_____ a. How did Hezekiah prepare to fight the Assyrians?

_____ b. What did he say to the people?

_____ c. What did the king of Assyria do to trouble Jerusalem?

_____ d. What did Hezekiah and Isaiah do?

_____ e. What did the Lord do to the Assyrians?

_____ f. What happened to their king?

_____ g. Why was the Lord's wrath kindled against Hezekiah?

_____ h. What did Hezekiah and the inhabitants of Jerusalem do?

_____ i. What did Hezekiah do with the "watercourse of Gihon"? (2 Chronicles 32:30.)

_____ j. Why did God leave Hezekiah when the Babylonians visited him?

_____ k. Where did Isaiah write about Hezekiah? (See Isaiah 37–39.)

---

2 Chronicles 33

_____ a. How did Manasseh anger the Lord?

_____ b. How did Manasseh and the people receive the Lord's warning?

_____ c. What did the Assyrians do to Manasseh? (See also 2 Chronicles 33:11a.)

_____ d. How did Manasseh know the Lord was his God?

_____ e. What did Amon do to anger the Lord?

_____ f. What happened to Amon?

_____ g. What did the people do at the death of Amon?

2 Chronicles 34

VERSE NUMBER

_____ a. What did Josiah do in the eighth year of his reign? in the twelfth year of his reign? in the eighteenth year of his reign?

_____ b. What book was brought to the king?

_____ c. Why did Josiah send his servants to inquire of the Lord?

_____ d. What was the Lord's message to the king?

_____ e. What covenant did Josiah and the people make with the Lord?

2 Chronicles 35

VERSE NUMBER

_____ a. What did Josiah instruct the Levites to do?

_____ b. When did Josiah keep the passover?

_____ c. What message did Necho, king of Egypt, send to Josiah?

_____ d. What happened to Josiah? Why?

2 Chronicles 36

VERSE NUMBER

_____ a. How did Jehoiakim, brother of Jehoahaz, become king?

_____ b. What happened to Jehoahaz?

_____ c. What happened to Jehoiakim? Why?

_____ d. What happened to Jehoiachin?

_____ e. Which prophet did Zedekiah reject?

_____ f. Whose families did the Lord lead out of Jerusalem? (See Helaman 6:10; see also 1 Nephi 1:4; 2:1–4; Helaman 8:21–22.)

_____ g. Why did the Lord try to turn the people from their wickedness?

_____ h. What happened to Jerusalem? to its inhabitants? to the temple?

_____ i. What did Cyrus, king of Persia, proclaim?

EZRA

Introduction

See Bible Dictionary, page 669, s.v. "Ezra."

_____ a. Who was Ezra?

_____ b. What was his mission?

_____ c. What was he allowed to do in 485 B.C.?

_____ d. What was his first reform when he arrived in Jerusalem?

_____ e. How did the Mosaic law become the center of Jewish life?

_____ f. What do the first six chapters of the book of Ezra contain?

_____ g. List four religious values taught in the book of Ezra.

Ezra 1

_____ a. What did King Cyrus proclaim? (See also Map 12.)

_____ b. Who went to Jerusalem?

_____ c. Who helped them? How?

_____ d. What did Cyrus donate for the temple?

Ezra 2

_____ a. Who are listed in Ezra 2?

_____ b. How long would those whose genealogy was lost have to wait to have the priesthood?

_____ c. How many people returned from captivity?

_____ d. What did some of the "chief of the fathers" do when they arrived in Jerusalem? (V. 68.)

Ezra 3

_____ a. What did Jeshua, the priests, and Zerubbabel and his brethren build?

_____ b. Which feast did the people observe?

_____ c. What came from Lebanon for the temple?

_____ d. What did the people do when the foundation of the temple was laid?

Ezra 4

_____ a. How did the Samaritans first try to stop the building of the temple? (See also Ezra 4:4a.)

_____ b. List four accusations the Samaritans made in the letter to Artaxerxes, king of Persia.

_____ c. What did the king reply?

_____ d. What happened to the work on the temple? by what means?

Ezra 5

_____ a. Who helped the Jews build the temple?

_____ b. What did Tatnai, the governor, write to King Darius? (See also Ezra 5:3a.)

Ezra 6

_____ a. What was written on the roll at Achmetha?

_____ b. What were Tatnai and his companions told to do?

_____ c. What was to happen to those who interrupted the building of the temple?

_____ d. What did Tatnai and his companions do?

_____ e. What did the elders of the Jews do?

_____ f. What did the children of Israel do when the temple was built?

_____ g. Who ate the passover meal?

Ezra 7

_____ a. Who was the chief priest Ezra was a descendent of?

_____ b. What had the king granted to Ezra? Why?

_____ c. What had Ezra prepared his heart to do?

_____ d. List six things that King Artaxerxes wrote to Ezra to do.

_____ e. How was Ezra blessed?

130

Ezra 8

VERSE NUMBER

_____ a. Who are listed in Ezra 8?

_____ b. Why did Ezra proclaim a fast at the river of Ahava? (See vv. 21–23, 21*b*.)

_____ c. Why did Ezra write that "the hand of our God was upon us"? (V. 31.)

Ezra 9

VERSE NUMBER

_____ a. What did the princes say to Ezra that caused him to rend his garment?

_____ b. How had the Lord extended his mercy to his people?

_____ c. How had the people forsaken the commandments?

_____ d. Why were the people unable to stand before God at that time?

Ezra 10

VERSE NUMBER

_____ a. What did Shechaniah suggest be done?

_____ b. What proclamation was made?

_____ c. What did Ezra say to the congregation?

_____ d. What did the congregation reply?

The Book of NEHEMIAH

Introduction

See Bible Dictionary, page 738, s.v. "Nehemiah."

_____ a. Who was Nehemiah?

_____ b. What was Nehemiah commissioned to do?

_____ c. What account does the book of Nehemiah contain?

_____ d. What are the four parts of the book?

Nehemiah 1

_____ a. What did Nehemiah do for the Jews in Jerusalem? Why?

_____ b. What had the Lord promised Moses?

_____ c. What did Nehemiah ask of the Lord?

Nehemiah 2

_____ a. What did Nehemiah ask of the King?

_____ b. How did Sanballat and Tobiah receive the news about Nehemiah?

_____ c. What did Nehemiah say to the rulers in Jerusalem?

_____ d. How did the rulers respond?

Nehemiah 3

_____ a. Who are listed in Nehemiah 3?

Nehemiah 4

_____ a. What did Sanballat and Tobiah conspire to do?

_____ b. What did the men of Judah do?

_____ c. What did Nehemiah say to them? (See also Alma 46:12.)

_____ d. How did the workers prepare to defend themselves?

Nehemiah 5

_____ a. Why did Nehemiah become very angry?

_____ b. What did Nehemiah ask the nobles to do?

_____ c. Why did Nehemiah call the priests?

_____ d. What did Nehemiah do that was different from what the previous governors had done? (See also Nehemiah 5:15a.)

Nehemiah 6

_____ a. Why did Sanballat and Tobiah want to meet Nehemiah?

_____ b. Why were all the enemies of Nehemiah and the Jews disappointed?

_____ c. Why did Tobiah send letters to the nobles in Judah and to Nehemiah?

Nehemiah 7

_____ a. Why did Nehemiah give Hanani and Hananiah charge of Jerusalem?

_____ b. What did Nehemiah say to them?

_____ c. Whose genealogy is in Nehemiah 7?

_____ d. Why were some priests denied the priesthood?

_____ e. When would they receive the priesthood?

Nehemiah 8

_____ a. What did Ezra read to the people? (See also Deuteronomy 31:10–13.)

_____ b. How was the book read? (See also Nehemiah 8:8c.)

_____ c. Why did the people weep?

_____ d. What event was held on the eighth day?

Nehemiah 9

_____ a. What did the people do on the twenty-fourth day of the month?

_____ b. List several things the Jews recited that the Lord had done for them.

_____ c. Why did the people make "a sure covenant"? (Nehemiah 9:38.)

Nehemiah 10

VERSE NUMBER

_____ a. What four things did the people covenant to do? (See also Nehemiah 10:29a.)

Nehemiah 11

VERSE NUMBER

_____ a. How was it decided who should dwell in Jerusalem?

Nehemiah 12

VERSE NUMBER

_____ a. Who are those named in Nehemiah 12?

_____ b. What was dedicated?

_____ c. What offices were appointed in the temple?

Nehemiah 13

VERSE NUMBER

_____ a. Why was the "mixed multitude" separated from Israel? (Nehemiah 13:3.)

_____ b. What had Eliashib the priest done for Tobiah?

_____ c. What did Nehemiah do upon his return from the king?

_____ d. Why did the merchants come no more upon the Sabbath?

_____ e. What did Nehemiah do about intermarriage?

The Book of ESTHER

Introduction

See Bible Dictionary, page 667, s.v. "Esther, Book of."

_____ a. In what period of Jewish history did the events in the book of Esther occur?

_____ b. Why did the Jews observe two days of feasting every year?

_____ c. Why is this book included in the Bible?

Esther 1

VERSE NUMBER

_____ a. How big was the kingdom of king Ahasuerus? (See also Map 12.)

_____ b. Why did the king command his chamberlains to bring Vashti, his wife, to him?

_____ c. Why was Vashti removed as queen?

Esther 2

VERSE NUMBER

_____ a. What did the king's servants suggest that the king do?

_____ b. Who was Mordecai?

_____ c. What did Hegai do for Esther? Why?

_____ d. Why was Esther made queen?

_____ e. How did Mordecai save the king's life?

Esther 3

VERSE NUMBER

_____ a. Why was Haman full of wrath?

_____ b. What did Haman obtain permission from the king to do?

Esther 4

VERSE NUMBER

_____ a. What message did Mordecai give to Esther?

_____ b. What could happen if one went into the inner court unto the king?

_____ c. What did Esther ask Mordecai to do?

Esther 5

_____ a. What did the king do when he saw Esther standing in the inner court?

_____ b. What did Esther ask of the king?

_____ c. Why did Haman order the gallows to be made?

Esther 6

_____ a. How was the king brought to remember Mordecai?

_____ b. Why did Haman visit the king?

_____ c. What did the king command Haman to do?

Esther 7

_____ a. What did Esther say to the king at the banquet?

_____ b. What happened to Haman?

Esther 8

_____ a. What happened to Mordecai?

_____ b. What did Esther ask of the king?

_____ c. What did the king say to Esther and Mordecai?

_____ d. What message did Mordecai have sent throughout the kingdom in the name of the king?

Esther 9

_____ a. Who helped the Jews? Why?

_____ b. What happened to the ten sons of Haman?

_____ c. How many enemies did the Jews slay in the other provinces?

_____ d. What message did Mordecai send to all the Jews in the kingdom?

_____ e. What feast did the Jews institute in the time of Esther? Why?

Esther 10

_____ a. What happened to Mordecai?

The Book of JOB

Introduction

See Bible Dictionary, page 713, s.v. "Job, Book of."

_____ a. What is narrated and discussed in the book of Job?

_____ b. What did Job's three friends discuss with him?

_____ c. What was the reason his friends gave for his suffering that Job would not agree to?

_____ d. What question is not entirely answered by the book of Job?

_____ e. What does the book of Job suggest are the purposes for affliction?

_____ f. List three high points of the book.

_____ g. How was Job able to endure the trials that came upon him?

Job 1

_____ a. How great a man was Job?

_____ b. Where had Satan been before meeting the Lord?

_____ c. What did Satan ask the Lord to do?

_____ d. What power did the Lord give to Satan?

_____ e. What news did the four messengers bring Job?

_____ f. How did Job respond?

Job 2

_____ a. What did Satan ask the Lord to do to Job?

_____ b. What power did the Lord give to Satan?

_____ c. What did Satan do to Job?

_____ d. What did Job's wife say to him?

_____ e. What did Job reply?

_____ f. What did Job's three friends do? Why?

Job 3

_____ a. What did Job curse?

_____ b. What did Job ask about his birth?

Job 4

_____ a. How did Eliphaz reprove Job?

Job 5

_____ a. What counsel did Eliphaz give to Job?

Job 6

_____ a. What did Job ask of the Lord?

_____ b. What did Job ask of his friends?

Job 7

_____ a. What did Job ask of the Lord?

Job 8

VERSE NUMBER

_____ a. What did Bildad say about God to Job?

Job 9

VERSE NUMBER

_____ a. What did Job acknowledge in Job 9?

Job 10

VERSE NUMBER

_____ a. What did Job acknowledge?

_____ b. What did Job ask God?

Job 11

VERSE NUMBER

_____ a. Why did Zophar condemn Job?

_____ b. What did Zophar counsel Job to do?

Job 12

VERSE NUMBER

_____ a. What did Job answer?

Job 13

VERSE NUMBER

_____ a. How much did Job trust in the Lord?

Job 14

VERSE NUMBER

_____ a. What did Job ask?

_____ b. What did Job answer?

Job 15

_____ a. What did Eliphaz say of wicked men?

Job 16

_____ a. What did Job testify of to his friends?

Job 17

_____ a. What did Job speak of in Job 17?

Job 18

_____ a. What did Bildad tell of in Job 18?

Job 19

_____ a. What did Job know to be true?

Job 20

_____ a. What did Zophar say of the wicked and the hypocrite?

Job 21

_____ a. What did Job admit?

_____ b. What did Job testify of?

Job 22

_____ a. What did Eliphaz accuse Job of?

_____ b. What did Eliphaz exhort Job to do?

Job 23

_____ a. What did Job do?

_____ b. What did Job say about his future? Why?

Job 24

_____ a. What will happen to the wicked?

Job 25

_____ a. What did Bildad do in Job 25?

Job 26

_____ a. What question did Job ask Bildad in Job 26?

Job 27

_____ a. What did Job say of the wicked?

Job 28

_____ a. Where does wealth come from?

_____ b. What cannot be purchased?

_____ c. How did Job define wisdom and understanding?

Job 29

_____ a. Why had Job been blessed in the past?

b. How had Job helped the poor and needy?

Job 30

_____ a. Who persecuted Job?

_____ b. Whom had Job comforted?

Job 31

_____ a. What did Job invite God to do? Why?

Job 32

_____ a. What did Elihu say about wisdom to Job?

Job 33

_____ a. What did Elihu say about God to Job?

Job 34

_____ a. What did Elihu teach about God in Job 34?

Job 35

_____ a. What may our wickedness or righteousness do for other people?

Job 36

_____ a. What does God do for the righteous?

_____ b. What happens to the wicked?

Job 37

_____ a. What does the Lord control?

_____ b. How does God reign?

Job 38

_____ a. What did God ask Job?

_____ b. What do the phenomena of nature show?

Job 39

_____ a. What is compared to God's mighty works?

Job 40

_____ a. What did Job do when the Lord challenged him?

_____ b. What did the Lord speak of to Job?

Job 41

_____ a. What things are the Lord's?

_____ b. What is leviathan? (See Bible Dictionary, p. 724, s.v. "Leviathan.")

Job 42

_____ a. Whom did Job see?

_____ b. What did Job do?

_____ c. What did the Lord tell Job's three friends to do?

_____ d. How did the Lord bless Job for his faithfulness?

The Book of PSALMS

Introduction

See Bible Dictionary, page 754, s.v. "Psalms."

_____ a. What are the psalms called collectively in Hebrew?

_____ b. How many references to psalms are in the New Testament?

_____ c. How were many of the psalms to be accompanied?

_____ d. How many psalms are ascribed to David?

Psalm 1

VERSE NUMBER

_____ a. Who is blessed?

_____ b. How will he be blessed?

_____ c. What will the ungodly be like?

Psalm 2

VERSE NUMBER

_____ a. What counsel is given to kings and judges?

Psalm 3

VERSE NUMBER

_____ a. Why does David trust the Lord?

Psalm 4

VERSE NUMBER

_____ a. What does David plead for in Psalm 4?

Psalm 5

VERSE NUMBER

_____ a. Who should rejoice and shout for joy?

Psalm 6

VERSE NUMBER

_____ a. Why does David ask the Lord for mercy?

Psalm 7

VERSE NUMBER

_____ a. What does David ask the Lord?

Psalm 8

VERSE NUMBER

_____ a. What does David ask the Lord?

_____ b. What has God made man to be? (See Psalm 8:5a.)

_____ c. What does man have dominion over?

Psalm 9

VERSE NUMBER

_____ a. Why does David praise the Lord?

Psalm 10

VERSE NUMBER

_____ a. What does David say about the wicked?

Psalm 11

_____ a. What does the Lord do for the righteous? for the wicked?

Psalm 12

_____ a. What do the children of men do?

Psalm 13

_____ a. Why does David rejoice?

Psalm 14

_____ a. What does the fool say in his heart?

Psalm 15

_____ a. What does David ask the Lord? (See also Psalm 15:1b.)

_____ b. How does David answer?

Psalm 16

_____ a. Where is fulness of joy to be found?

Psalm 17

_____ a. Why does David plead with the Lord?

Psalm 18

_____ a. Why does David praise the Lord?

Psalm 19

_____ a. What three things does David testify of?

Psalm 20

_____ a. What will the Lord do for his anointed?

Psalm 21

_____ a. What does David tell of in Psalm 21?

Psalm 22

_____ a. What does David foretell in this psalm?

_____ b. Whom is David quoting in verses 1 and 16?

_____ c. Why will all the kindreds of the nations worship before the Lord?

Psalm 23

_____ a. Who is David's shepherd?

_____ b. List five things the Lord will do for David.

_____ c. What does David expect of the Lord?

Psalm 24

_____ a. To whom does the earth and its fulness belong? Why?

_____ b. Who will receive the blessing from the Lord?

Psalm 25

_____ a. For whom are mercy and truth?

Psalm 26

_____ a. What does David say of himself in Psalm 26?

Psalm 27

_____ a. What is the Lord to David?

_____ b. What is the one thing David has sought from the Lord?

_____ c. Why should we wait on the Lord?

Psalm 28

_____ a. What does David pray for in Psalm 28?

Psalm 29

_____ a. How should we worship the Lord?

Psalm 30

_____ a. What does David include in his song?

Psalm 31

_____ a. What are we counseled to do?

Psalm 32

_____ a. Who does David say is blessed? (See also Psalm 32:1a.)

Psalm 33

_____ a. Which nation is blessed?

Psalm 34

_____ a. What does David counsel the saints to do?

Psalm 35

_____ a. What had David's enemies done to him?

Psalm 36

_____ a. For what does David praise the Lord?

Psalm 37

_____ a. Who will "soon be cut down like the grass"? (Psalm 37:2.)

_____ b. What counsel does David give?

_____ c. Why will the Lord deliver the righteous in the time of trouble?

Psalm 38

_____ a. What does David say of his enemies?

Psalm 39

_____ a. What does David seek to control?

Psalm 40

_____ a. What would the Messiah do when he came?

Psalm 41

_____ a. Whom will the Lord deliver in time of trouble?

Psalm 42

_____ a. What do the souls of the righteous thirst for?

Psalm 43

_____ a. What does the psalmist ask to be sent? Why?

Psalm 44

_____ a. What do the saints do in Psalm 44?

Psalm 45

VERSE NUMBER

_____ a. Whose name will be remembered in all generations?

Psalm 46

VERSE NUMBER

_____ a. What does Psalm 46 reveal about God?

Psalm 47

VERSE NUMBER

_____ a. Why is God to be praised?

Psalm 48

VERSE NUMBER

_____ a. What will be established forever?

Psalm 49

VERSE NUMBER

_____ a. When will the glory of the rich man cease?

Psalm 50

VERSE NUMBER

_____ a. Which saints are to gather unto the Lord?

Psalm 51

VERSE NUMBER

_____ a. What is David pleading for? (See also 2 Samuel 11:26–27.)

_____ b. What sacrifice does God require?

Psalm 52

_____ a. What do wicked tongues do?

Psalm 53

_____ a. What does the fool say in his heart?

Psalm 54

_____ a. For what does David plead unto the Lord?

Psalm 55

_____ a. When does David pray? Why?

Psalm 56

_____ a. What does David do in Psalm 56?

Psalm 57

_____ a. What does David acclaim in Psalm 57?

Psalm 58

_____ a. What do wicked judges do?

Psalm 59

_____ a. What does David pray for?

Psalm 60

_____ a. Where does the Lord place Ephraim?

Psalm 61

_____ a. Where does David find shelter?

Psalm 62

_____ a. How is every person rewarded?

Psalm 63

_____ a. For whom does David thirst?

Psalm 64

_____ a. What will the righteous do?

Psalm 65

_____ a. What does David speak of in Psalm 65?

Psalm 66

_____ a. How are men compared to silver?

Psalm 67

_____ a. How will the Lord judge the people?

Psalm 68

_____ a. What does the God of Israel give to his people?

Psalm 69

_____ a. What will God do for Zion and the cities of Judah? (See also Psalm 69:35b.)

Psalm 70

_____ a. What does David proclaim?

Psalm 71

_____ a. How does David praise God?

Psalm 72

_____ a. What will Solomon do for the poor?

Psalm 73

_____ a. Who will be received up into glory?

Psalm 74

_____ a. What do the wicked do?

Psalm 75

_____ a. What do the righteous do?

Psalm 76

VERSE NUMBER

_____ a. Whom will God save?

Psalm 77

VERSE NUMBER

_____ a. Who cry unto the Lord?

Psalm 78

VERSE NUMBER

_____ a. What must Israel teach to their children?

Psalm 79

VERSE NUMBER

_____ a. What does Israel plead for?

Psalm 80

VERSE NUMBER

_____ a. What does Israel plead with the Lord for in Psalm 80?

Psalm 81

VERSE NUMBER

_____ a. What would Israel have done if they had walked in the Lord's ways?

Psalm 82

VERSE NUMBER

_____ a. What does the Lord say in verse 6?

Psalm 83

VERSE NUMBER

_____ a. Who is the most high over all the earth? (See also Psalm 83:18a.)

Psalm 84

VERSE NUMBER

_____ a. What will be given to those who walk uprightly?

Psalm 85

VERSE NUMBER

_____ a. What will spring out of the earth?

Psalm 86

VERSE NUMBER

_____ a. Who will worship before God?

Psalm 87

VERSE NUMBER

_____ a. Who will establish Zion?

Psalm 88

VERSE NUMBER

_____ a. Whose prayer is this?

Psalm 89

VERSE NUMBER

_____ a. What does this song set forth?

Psalm 90

VERSE NUMBER

_____ a. What does Moses implore the Lord to do?

Psalm 91

VERSE NUMBER

_____ a. Who will be delivered and honored?

Psalm 92

_____ a. What is a good thing to do?

Psalm 93

_____ a. What will become of the Lord's house forever?

Psalm 94

_____ a. Who will be blessed?

Psalm 95

_____ a. What happened because Israel provoked the Lord?

Psalm 96

_____ a. What will the Lord do when he comes?

Psalm 97

_____ a. Who hates evil?

Psalm 98

_____ a. Why should the righteous sing praises to the Lord?

Psalm 99

_____ a. Who is great in Zion?

Psalm 100

_____ a. How are we to serve the Lord?

_____ b. Why should we be thankful to him?

Psalm 101

_____ a. What does David sing of in this psalm?

Psalm 102

_____ a. What will happen when Zion is built up by the Lord?

Psalm 103

_____ a. To whom is the Lord merciful?

Psalm 104

_____ a. With what is the Lord clothed?

Psalm 105

_____ a. How does the Lord instruct kings on behalf of his servants?

Psalm 106

_____ a. Why was Israel scattered and slain?

Psalm 107

_____ a. What do we need to do?

Psalm 108

_____ a. How is Judah the Lord's lawgiver?

Psalm 109

_____ a. What does David speak of in Psalm 109?

Psalm 110

_____ a. What will Christ be forever?

Psalm 111

_____ a. How is the Lord described?

Psalm 112

_____ a. Who is to be blessed? How?

Psalm 113

_____ a. Why are we to praise the Lord and bless his name?

Psalm 114

_____ a. Who governs the land and sea? Why?

Psalm 115

_____ a. What are idols?

Psalm 116

_____ a. What is precious in the sight of the Lord?

Psalm 117

_____ a. Why is the Lord to be praised?

Psalm 118

_____ a. Why is all Israel to give thanks to the Lord?

Psalm 119

_____ a. Who are blessed?

_____ b. How has the psalmist sought the Lord?

_____ c. What are the psalmist's "delight and [his] counsellors"? (Psalm 119:24; see also 2 Nephi 4:15.)

_____ d. What way has the psalmist chosen?

_____ e. In verses 33 through 40, what does the psalmist ask of the Lord? Why?

_____ f. Where would the psalmist speak of the Lord's testimonies?

_____ g. How has the psalmist been comforted?

_____ h. Who were the psalmist's companions?

_____ i. What does the psalmist ask the Lord to teach him?

_____ j. What does the psalmist ask to be given him? Why?

_____ k. Why does the psalmist ask the Lord's help?

_____ l. What prevents the psalmist from perishing in his affliction?

_____ m. Why does the psalmist "hate every false way"? (V. 104.)

_____ n. What is the word of the Lord to the psalmist? (See also Alma 37:44.)

_____ o. Why does the psalmist want the Lord to hold him up?

_____ p. How much does the psalmist love the commandments of the Lord?

_____ q. In verse 133, what does the psalmist request of the Lord?

_____ r. In verse 144, what does the psalmist request of the Lord?

_____ s. Who were "draw[ing] nigh" to the psalmist? (V. 150.)

_____ t. In verses 153 through 156, what does the psalmist ask of the Lord?

_____ u. What will they have who "love thy law"? (V. 165.)

_____ v. In verses 169 through 176, what does the psalmist plead for the Lord to do?

Psalm 120

VERSE NUMBER

_____ a. What does the Lord do when the psalmist cries unto the Lord in distress?

Psalm 121

VERSE NUMBER

_____ a. Where does our help come from?

Psalm 122

VERSE NUMBER

_____ a. What does David say in Psalm 122?

Psalm 123

VERSE NUMBER

_____ a. What does the psalmist ask of the Lord?

Psalm 124

VERSE NUMBER

_____ a. Who is the "help" of Israel? (Psalm 124:8.)

Psalm 125

VERSE NUMBER

_____ a. Who are to be blessed?

Psalm 126

VERSE NUMBER

_____ a. What has the Lord done for his people?

Psalm 127

VERSE NUMBER

_____ a. Who labors in vain?

_____ b. What are a "heritage of the Lord"? (Psalm 127:3.)

_____ c. Which man is happy?

Psalm 128

VERSE NUMBER

_____ a. Who are blessed?

Psalm 129

VERSE NUMBER

_____ a. What is to happen to those who hate Zion?

Psalm 130

VERSE NUMBER

_____ a. What three things does the psalmist pray for?

Psalm 131

VERSE NUMBER

_____ a. What does David say about Israel?

Psalm 132

VERSE NUMBER

_____ a. What does the Lord swear unto David?

Psalm 133

VERSE NUMBER

_____ a. What is it good for the brethren to do?

Psalm 134

_____ a. What are the servants of the Lord instructed to do in Psalm 134?

Psalm 135

_____ a. What are some of the great things the Lord has done?

_____ b. Why are idols not to be trusted?

Psalm 136

_____ a. Why should we give thanks to God?

Psalm 137

_____ a. Why did the Jews weep beside the waters of Babylon?

Psalm 138

_____ a. Why does David praise the Lord?

Psalm 139

_____ a. What does David ask the Lord?

Psalm 140

_____ a. What does David pray for?

_____ b. Who will maintain the cause of the afflicted and poor?

Psalm 141

VERSE NUMBER

_____ a. What does David pray for in Psalm 141?

Psalm 142

VERSE NUMBER

_____ a. What does David pray for in Psalm 142?

Psalm 143

VERSE NUMBER

_____ a. What does David meditate on?

Psalm 144

VERSE NUMBER

_____ a. Who are happy?

Psalm 145

VERSE NUMBER

_____ a. Who is the Lord "nigh unto"? (Psalm 145:18.)

_____ b. Whom will the Lord preserve?

Psalm 146

VERSE NUMBER

_____ a. The Lord does what for the needy?

Psalm 147

VERSE NUMBER

_____ a. Why should we praise the Lord?

_____ b. With whom is the Lord pleased?

Psalm 148

_____ a. Who are to praise the Lord?

Psalm 149

_____ a. What will the Lord do for the meek?

Psalm 150

_____ a. Why and how is the Lord to be praised?

_____ b. Who is to praise the Lord?

The PROVERBS

Introduction

See Bible Dictionary, page 754, s.v. "Proverbs."

_____ a. What does the book of Proverbs contain?

_____ b. What is taken for granted throughout the book?

_____ c. List the four sections of the book.

Proverbs 1

_____ a. What is the beginning of knowledge? (See also Proverbs 1:7a.)

_____ b. What do fools despise?

_____ c. Whose instructions and laws should be obeyed?

_____ d. What should we do when sinners entice us?

_____ e. Who will dwell safely and not fear evil?

Proverbs 2

VERSE NUMBER

_____ a. How will we find the "knowledge of God"? (Proverbs 2:5.)

_____ b. What is *frowardness*? (See v. 14*a*.)

_____ c. What way should we walk in?

_____ d. Who will dwell and remain in the land?

Proverbs 3

VERSE NUMBER

_____ a. Whom are we to trust? How much?

_____ b. With what are we to honor the Lord? Why?

_____ c. What does the Lord do to those he loves?

_____ d. Who is more precious than rubies?

_____ e. Who shall inherit glory?

Proverbs 4

VERSE NUMBER

_____ a. What are we to seek after in this life? Why?

_____ b. What is the path of the just?

_____ c. What is the way of the wicked?

Proverbs 5

VERSE NUMBER

_____ a. Whose ways are before the Lord?

_____ b. How will the wicked be bound?

Proverbs 6

_____ a. What seven things does the Lord hate?

_____ b. What happens to a person who commits adultery?

Proverbs 7

_____ a. How does a whorish woman lead a man?

_____ b. What is the way to hell?

Proverbs 8

_____ a. What is to be greatly desired?

_____ b. What did the Lord and the sons of men possess in the premortal existence?

Proverbs 9

_____ a. What happens when we reprove a scorner?

_____ b. What happens when we rebuke a wise man?

_____ c. What will a wise man do when he is instructed?

_____ d. Where do the guests of a foolish woman go?

Proverbs 10

_____ a. What does a wise son do for his father?

_____ b. Where is wisdom found?

_____ c. What do wise men do?

Proverbs 11

_____ a. Who despises his neighbor?

_____ b. Where is safety?

_____ c. What does a gracious woman retain?

_____ d. What is like a fair woman without discretion?

_____ e. Who shall inherit the wind?

Proverbs 12

_____ a. Who loves knowledge?

_____ b. Who is a crown to a man?

_____ c. Who regards the life of his beast?

_____ d. In whose eyes is the way of the fool right?

_____ e. What are an abomination to the Lord?

Proverbs 13

_____ a. What does a wise son do?

_____ b. How does contention come?

_____ c. What will happen to those who refuse instruction?

_____ d. Why should we walk with wise men?

_____ e. What does a man do who loves his son?

Proverbs 14

_____ a. What will a faithful witness refuse to do?

_____ b. Who believes every word?

_____ c. What does a prudent man do?

_____ d. Who is happy?

_____ e. How is money to be acquired?

_____ f. What exalts a nation? (See Proverbs 14:34a.)

_____ g. Whom does the king favor?

Proverbs 15

_____ a. What turns away wrath?

_____ b. What stirs up anger?

_____ c. To whom will a scorner not go?

_____ d. What is established in the multitude of counselors?

_____ e. What are the "thoughts of the wicked" to the Lord? (Proverbs 15:26.)

_____ f. What is before honor?

Proverbs 16

_____ a. Who are an abomination to the Lord?

_____ b. What is better to get than gold and silver?

_____ c. What "goeth before destruction"? (Proverbs 16:18.)

_____ d. Who shall find good?

_____ e. What does a violent man do?

_____ f. What is a hoary head? (See v. 31a.)

_____ g. Who is better than the mighty and "he that taketh a city"? (V. 32.)

Proverbs 17

_____ a. Who are the crown of old men?

_____ b. Who are the glory of children?

_____ c. When will evil not depart from a person's house?

_____ d. Who are an abomination to the Lord?

_____ e. Who "spareth his words"? (Proverbs 17:27.)

_____ f. When is a fool counted wise?

Proverbs 18

VERSE NUMBER

_____ a. Who is the brother of the lazy? (See also Proverbs 18:9a, b.)

_____ b. Why should we listen carefully to a matter before answering?

_____ c. What is harder to be won than a strong city?

_____ d. Who "hath obtained favor of the Lord"? (V. 22a.)

_____ e. What must we do to have friends?

Proverbs 19

VERSE NUMBER

_____ a. When is it better to be poor?

_____ b. Where is a prudent wife from?

_____ c. Who will repay the man who lends to the poor?

_____ d. Why should we hear counsel and receive instruction?

Proverbs 20

VERSE NUMBER

_____ a. Who is not wise?

_____ b. Where is the glory of young men?

Proverbs 21

VERSE NUMBER

_____ a. What is more acceptable to the Lord than sacrifice?

_____ b. What does the soul of the wicked desire?

_____ c. What will happen to him who "stoppeth his ears at the cry of the poor"? (Proverbs 21:13.)

_____ d. Who will be poor?

_____ e. What does a foolish man do with his treasure and oil?

_____ f. Where is victory in the day of battle? (See also v. 31*b.*)

Proverbs 22

_____ a. What is better than great riches and silver and gold?

_____ b. What will a child not do if he is trained in the way he should go?

_____ c. What will drive foolishness far from a child? (See also Proverbs 23:13–14.)

_____ d. What will happen to those who oppress the poor?

Proverbs 23

_____ a. Whose bread are we not to eat? Why?

_____ b. Why should we not speak to the ears of the fool?

_____ c. Whom should our hearts not envy?

_____ d. Whom are we to "be not among"? (Proverbs 23:20.) Why?

_____ e. How are we to treat our parents?

Proverbs 24

_____ a. Where is safety?

_____ b. Who is called a mischievous person?

_____ c. Why should we not fret because of evil men?

Proverbs 25

_____ a. Why should we not stand in the place of great men?

_____ b. What is confidence in an unfaithful man like in time of trouble?

_____ c. What should we do when our enemy is hungry and thirsty?

_____ d. What is like a man who does not discipline himself?

Proverbs 26

_____ a. Why should we not answer a fool "according to his folly"? (Proverbs 26:4.)

_____ b. What causes strife? (See also v. 20a.)

_____ c. What will happen to him who "diggeth a pit" or "rolleth a stone"? (V. 27.)

Proverbs 27

_____ a. What does a prudent man do about evil?

_____ b. What is never full? (See Proverbs 27:20a.)

Proverbs 28

_____ a. When do the wicked flee?

_____ b. Who does not understand judgment?

_____ c. Who will receive mercy?

_____ d. Who shall be delivered?

_____ e. Who will not lack?

Proverbs 29

_____ a. What do the people do when the righteous are in authority?

_____ b. What do the people do when the wicked rule?

_____ c. Who considers the cause of the poor?

_____ d. When do the people perish? (See also Proverbs 29:18a, b.)

_____ e. What will pride do to a man?

Proverbs 30

VERSE NUMBER

_____ a. What is Proverbs 30?

_____ b. What two things did Agur require of the Lord before he died?

_____ c. What four things are "too wonderful"? (V. 18.)

Proverbs 31

VERSE NUMBER

_____ a. What is Proverbs 31?

_____ b. What two things was Lemuel not to do?

_____ c. Whose cause was Lemuel to plead?

_____ d. Whose price is far above rubies?

_____ e. Which women will be praised?

ECCLESIASTES; or, the Preacher

Introduction

See Bible Dictionary, page 659, s.v. "Ecclesiastes."

_____ a. What does *ecclesiastes* mean?

_____ b. What problems are reflected upon in this book?

_____ c. What is in the epilogue?

_____ d. From what point of view was the book written?

_____ e. What does *vanity* mean?

_____ f. What do chapters 10 and 11 conclude?

173

Ecclesiastes 1

_____ a. Whose words are in Ecclesiastes 1?

_____ b. What is vanity? (See v. 2b.)

_____ c. What had the preacher given his heart to do? (See also v. 13b.)

_____ d. What is "in much wisdom"? (V. 18.)

Ecclesiastes 2

_____ a. What were vanity and vexation of spirit?

_____ b. What does God give to man?

Ecclesiastes 3

_____ a. What is there for everything?

_____ b. Whom will God judge?

Ecclesiastes 4

_____ a. What is vanity?

_____ b. What is better than an old and foolish king?

Ecclesiastes 5

_____ a. How is a fool's voice known?

_____ b. What are a gift from God?

Ecclesiastes 6

_____ a. What prevents a man's riches, wealth, honor, and posterity from being filled with vanity?

Ecclesiastes 7

_____ a. What does wisdom do for those who have it? (See also Ecclesiastes 7:12b.)

Ecclesiastes 8

_____ a. What do none have the power to avoid?

_____ b. Why are the wicked unable to find wisdom?

Ecclesiastes 9

_____ a. Who are in the hand of God?

_____ b. What is better than strength?

_____ c. Who is able to destroy much good?

Ecclesiastes 10

_____ a. What will destroy the reputation of the wise and honorable?

_____ b. Whose words are gracious?

_____ c. Who is full of words?

Ecclesiastes 11

_____ a. What are we encouraged to do?

_____ b. What will God do?

Ecclesiastes 12

_____ a. What will happen to the spirit at death?

_____ b. What are the words of the wise? (See also Ecclesiastes 12:11a.)

_____ c. What is the whole duty of man? (See also v. 14.)

The SONG OF SOLOMON

Introduction

See Bible Dictionary, page 776, s.v. "Song of Solomon."

_____ a. What does the Song of Solomon have in it?

_____ b. What does the manuscript of the Joseph Smith Translation say about the Song?

_____ c. Why has this Song remained in the canon of scripture?

The Book of the Prophet ISAIAH

Introduction

See Bible Dictionary, page 707, s.v. "Isaiah."

_____ a. What does *Isaiah* mean?

_____ b. When was Isaiah a prophet in Jerusalem?

_____ c. What influence did Isaiah have during the reign of Hezekiah? Why?

_____ d. According to tradition, how did Isaiah die?

_____ e. What did the Lord tell the Nephites about Isaiah? (See also 3 Nephi 23:1–3.)

_____ f. What two things do the writings and prophecies of Isaiah deal with?

_____ g. List the five parts of the major theme of his writings.

_____ h. What is a major difficulty in understanding the book?

_____ i. What is the best guide to understanding Isaiah?

_____ j. What will we more fully comprehend when we understand Isaiah?

Isaiah 1

VERSE NUMBER

_____ a. What were most of the people in Israel?

_____ b. How many were faithful?

_____ c. What were the faithful called upon to do?

_____ d. When will Zion be redeemed?

Isaiah 2

VERSE NUMBER

_____ a. List four things that Isaiah saw.

_____ b. What will happen to the proud and wicked at the Second Coming?

Isaiah 3

VERSE NUMBER

_____ a. Why will Judah and Jerusalem be punished?

_____ b. What will the Lord do for his people?

_____ c. What will happen to the daughters of Zion? Why?

Isaiah 4

VERSE NUMBER

_____ a. What will become of the daughters of Zion? When?

Isaiah 5

VERSE NUMBER

_____ a. What is the Lord's vineyard?

_____ b. What will happen to Israel?

Isaiah 6

_____ a. Whom does Isaiah see?

_____ b. What happened to his sins?

_____ c. What is he called to do?

_____ d. What is the live coal a symbol of? (See Isaiah 6:6a.)

Isaiah 7

_____ a. Who waged war against Judah? (See also Isaiah 7:2a.)

_____ b. Why is faith necessary? (See v. 9b.)

Isaiah 8

_____ a. What will the Lord be like? (See also Isaiah 8:14a.)

_____ b. Whom are we to seek?

_____ c. What should we turn to for guidance?

Isaiah 9

_____ a. Who will see a great light? (See also Isaiah 9:2a.)

_____ b. What is the burning? (See also v. 5b.)

_____ c. Who will reign on David's throne? (See also v. 6a.)

Isaiah 10

_____ a. What was the destruction by Assyria a type of?

_____ b. How many will be left on the earth at the Second Coming?

_____ c. Who will return in that day?

Isaiah 11

VERSE NUMBER

_____ a. Who is the stem of Jesse? (See also Isaiah 11:1d; D&C 113:1–2.)

_____ b. What will he do?

_____ c. What will cover the earth in the Millennium?

_____ d. What will the Lord do?

Isaiah 12

VERSE NUMBER

_____ a. What will all people do in the Millennium?

_____ b. Who will dwell among them?

Isaiah 13

VERSE NUMBER

_____ a. What was the destruction of Babylon a type of? (See also Isaiah 13:13c.)

_____ b. What will that day be like?

_____ c. What will fall forever?

Isaiah 14

VERSE NUMBER

_____ a. What will happen to Israel?

_____ b. Why was Lucifer cast out of heaven? (See also Isaiah 14:12c.)

_____ c. What will Israel triumph over?

Isaiah 15

VERSE NUMBER

_____ a. What would happen to Moab?

_____ b. What would the people of Moab do?

Isaiah 16

_____ a. What will the Messiah do when he sits upon David's throne?

Isaiah 17

_____ a. Why was Israel scattered?

_____ b. Who will be destroyed?

Isaiah 18

_____ a. What will the Lord raise up to the world?

Isaiah 19

_____ a. What will the Lord do to Egypt?

_____ b. Who will be blessed with Israel?

Isaiah 20

_____ a. What will Assyria do to Egypt?

Isaiah 21

_____ a. Who is fallen?

Isaiah 22

_____ a. What will happen to Jerusalem?

_____ b. What will happen to her people?

_____ c. List three things the Messiah will do. (See also Isaiah 22:22a.)

Isaiah 23

_____ a. What will happen to Tyre?

Isaiah 24

_____ a. What will men do?

_____ b. List three things that will happen at the Second Coming.

_____ c. Where will the Lord reign when he comes?

Isaiah 25

_____ a. What will the Lord prepare in Mount Zion?

_____ b. What will be said of the Lord?

Isaiah 26

_____ a. In whom are we to trust?

_____ b. What will Jehovah do?

_____ c. Who will rise in the resurrection?

Isaiah 27

_____ a. What will Israel do?

Isaiah 28

_____ a. What day is referred to in verse 5? (See Isaiah 28:5a.)

_____ b. Who is promised as "a sure foundation"? (V. 16.)

Isaiah 29

_____ a. Who will speak as a voice from the dust? (See also Isaiah 29:1a.)

_____ b. List three things that are foretold.

Isaiah 30

_____ a. What happened to Israel? Why?

_____ b. What will happen to Israel?

_____ c. When and why will the Lord come?

Isaiah 31

_____ a. Why was Israel reproved?

_____ b. What will the Lord do when he comes?

Isaiah 32

_____ a. What will the Messiah do when he comes?

_____ b. How long will the land of Israel be a wilderness?

Isaiah 33

_____ a. What will precede the Second Coming?

_____ b. What will come with the Lord?

_____ c. Who will be perfected?

_____ d. What will the Lord be?

Isaiah 34

_____ a. What will happen at the Second Coming?

_____ b. What will be upon all nations?

_____ c. Upon whom will the Lord's sword fall? (See also Bible Dictionary, p. 706, s.v. "Idumea.")

Isaiah 35

_____ a. List four things that will happen in the day of restoration.

Isaiah 36

_____ a. What did the Assyrians do?

Isaiah 37

_____ a. What two things did Hezekiah do?

_____ b. List three things that Isaiah prophesies.

_____ c. Who slayed the Assyrians?

_____ d. Who slayed Sennacherib?

Isaiah 38

_____ a. What sign was Hezekiah given that his life would be lengthened fifteen years?

_____ b. What did Hezekiah do?

Isaiah 39

_____ a. What did Hezekiah reveal to the Babylonians?

_____ b. What did Isaiah prophesy would happen?

Isaiah 40

_____ a. What was to be prepared?

_____ b. How great is Israel's God?

Isaiah 41

_____ a. What did the Lord say to Israel?

_____ b. What are idols?

Isaiah 42

_____ a. List three things the Lord will do. (See also Isaiah 42:7c.)

Isaiah 43

_____ a. List four things the Lord said to Israel.

Isaiah 44

_____ a. What will be poured out upon the seed of Israel?

_____ b. List two things the Lord will do.

Isaiah 45

_____ a. What will Cyrus do?

b. What will every tongue do? (See also Isaiah 45:23*b*.)

Isaiah 46

_____ a. What are not to be compared to the Lord?

_____ b. Who will save Israel?

Isaiah 47

_____ a. What will happen to Babylon and Chaldea? Why?

Isaiah 48

_____ a. What did the Lord reveal to Israel?

_____ b. Who have been chosen?

Isaiah 49

_____ a. What will happen to the prisoners?

_____ b. How will Israel be gathered in the last days?

_____ c. Who will help them?

Isaiah 50

_____ a. Who will have the tongue of the learned and not be confounded?

Isaiah 51

_____ a. What will the Lord do in the last days?

_____ b. Who will come to Zion?

Isaiah 52

_____ a. What will happen to Zion in the last days?

_____ b. What will happen to Jerusalem in the last days?

Isaiah 53

_____ a. What would the Messiah experience before his resurrection?

_____ b. What would he make his soul an offering for?

_____ c. For whom would he make intercession?

Isaiah 54

_____ a. What will happen to Zion and her stakes in the last days?

_____ b. How will Israel be gathered?

Isaiah 55

_____ a. What will the Lord make with Israel?

_____ b. What are we to do while the Lord is near?

Isaiah 56

_____ a. Who will be exalted?

_____ b. Whom will the Lord gather to the house of Israel?

Isaiah 57

_____ a. What will happen to the righteous?

_____ b. What is promised to the penitent?

_____ c. Who shall have no peace?

Isaiah 58

_____ a. What did the Lord expect on the day of the fast?

_____ b. What are the blessings of the fast?

_____ c. What should we do and refrain from doing on the Sabbath? Why?

Isaiah 59

_____ a. Why is Israel separated from their God?

_____ b. What testifies against them?

_____ c. List three things the Messiah will do.

Isaiah 60

_____ a. When will Israel rise again as a mighty nation?

_____ b. Who will join with Israel and serve her?

_____ c. What will be established?

_____ d. How shall they dwell?

Isaiah 61

_____ a. What three things will the Messiah do?

_____ b. What will the Lord do in the last days?

Isaiah 62

_____ a. Who will teach about the Lord?

_____ b. What will be established?

Isaiah 63

VERSE NUMBER

_____ a. What will the Second Coming be a day of?

_____ b. What will the Saints do?

Isaiah 64

VERSE NUMBER

_____ a. What did Israel pray for?

Isaiah 65

VERSE NUMBER

_____ a. Why was ancient Israel rejected?

_____ b. When will the Lord's people rejoice and triumph?

Isaiah 66

VERSE NUMBER

_____ a. What three events will happen at the Second Coming?

The Book of the Prophet JEREMIAH

Introduction

See Bible Dictionary, page 711, s.v. "Jeremiah."

_____ a. When did Jeremiah prophesy?

_____ b. What did he do after Josiah's death?

_____ c. Who were continuously opposed to him?

_____ d. According to tradition, how did Jeremiah die?

_____ e. When is "external service" useless?

_____ f. What are the five main divisions of the book of Jeremiah?

_____ g. List the themes of three notable passages in Jeremiah.

_____ h. Where else are some of Jeremiah's prophecies found?

Jeremiah 1

VERSE NUMBER

_____ a. What was Jeremiah foreordained to be?

_____ b. What was he called to do?

Jeremiah 2

VERSE NUMBER

_____ a. List three things the Jews did that offended the Lord.

Jeremiah 3

VERSE NUMBER

_____ a. What did Israel and Judah do?

_____ b. What would the Lord do in the last days?

Jeremiah 4

VERSE NUMBER

_____ a. Who were called to repentance?

_____ b. For what did Jeremiah lament?

Jeremiah 5

VERSE NUMBER

_____ a. What would be poured out upon the Jews? Why?

_____ b. What were withheld because of their iniquities?

Jeremiah 6

VERSE NUMBER

_____ a. What would happen to Jerusalem? Why?

Jeremiah 7

VERSE NUMBER

_____ a. Upon what condition would Jerusalem be preserved?

_____ b. What had the temple become?

_____ c. Why had the Lord rejected "that generation of Jews"? (Headnote to Jeremiah 7.)

_____ d. Whom did they offer as sacrifices?

Jeremiah 8

VERSE NUMBER

_____ a. What would happen to the inhabitants of Jerusalem?

Jeremiah 9

VERSE NUMBER

_____ a. What would happen to the people?

Jeremiah 10

VERSE NUMBER

_____ a. Why should Israel "learn not the way of the heathen"? (Jeremiah 10:2.)

Jeremiah 11

VERSE NUMBER

_____ a. Why were the Jews cursed?

_____ b. What was their penalty?

Jeremiah 12

VERSE NUMBER

_____ a. What did Jeremiah complain of?

_____ b. What must other nations do to be numbered with Israel?

Jeremiah 13

VERSE NUMBER

_____ a. How would Israel and Judah be "as this girdle, which is good for nothing"? (Jeremiah 13:10.)

_____ b. What would happen to Judah?

Jeremiah 14

VERSE NUMBER

_____ a. Why did Jeremiah pray?

_____ b. Why would the Lord refuse to hear the people?

Jeremiah 15

VERSE NUMBER

_____ a. List four things the Jews would suffer.

_____ b. Where would the Jews be scattered?

Jeremiah 16

VERSE NUMBER

_____ a. What would happen to Israel? Why?

_____ b. Who would gather Israel?

_____ c. What would be restored for the last time?

Jeremiah 17

VERSE NUMBER

_____ a. Why was Judah taken captive?

_____ b. What would save the people from destruction?

Jeremiah 18

_____ a. What was Israel in the hands of the Lord?

_____ b. Upon what condition would the Lord withhold "the evil decreed against" the nations? (Headnote to Jeremiah 18.)

_____ c. What would happen to the house of Judah?

Jeremiah 19

_____ a. What would the Lord bring upon Judah? Why?

_____ b. What would the Jews do in the siege?

Jeremiah 20

_____ a. What happened to Jeremiah?

_____ b. What did Jeremiah prophesy?

Jeremiah 21

_____ a. What did Jeremiah foretell?

_____ b. Whom would Nebuchadnezzar take captive?

Jeremiah 22

_____ a. What would determine whether David's throne stands or falls?

_____ b. What rested upon the kings of Judah?

Jeremiah 23

_____ a. Who would be gathered in the last days?

_____ b. Who would reign in righteousness?

_____ c. Who would be cursed?

Jeremiah 24

_____ a. What would happen to Zedekiah and the Jews?

_____ b. What would happen to some of the Jews?

Jeremiah 25

_____ a. How long would Judah serve Babylon?

_____ b. What would all the inhabitants of the earth be doing in the last days?

Jeremiah 26

_____ a. What did Jeremiah prophesy?

_____ b. What happened to him because of his prophecy?

Jeremiah 27

_____ a. What message did the Lord send to many nations?

Jeremiah 28

_____ a. What was Hananiah's false prophecy?

Jeremiah 29

_____ a. What did Jeremiah tell the Jews?

_____ b. What would happen to those who remained in Jerusalem?

_____ c. Who is cursed? Why?

Jeremiah 30

_____ a. What would happen to Judah and Israel in the last days?

_____ b. Who would reign over them?

Jeremiah 31

_____ a. Who has the birthright?

_____ b. What would the Lord make with the birthright people in the last days?

Jeremiah 32

_____ a. What did Zedekiah do to Jeremiah?

_____ b. What would the Lord do with Israel?

Jeremiah 33

_____ a. Who would be gathered?

_____ b. Who would reign forever?

Jeremiah 34

_____ a. What did Jeremiah prophesy of?

_____ b. What would happen to the Jews?

Jeremiah 35

_____ a. Why were the Rechabites commended and blessed?

_____ b. How would Jonadab be blessed? Why?

Jeremiah 36

_____ a. What did Baruch do?

_____ b. Why did judgment come upon Jehoiakim?

_____ c. What did Jeremiah do?

Jeremiah 37

_____ a. What did Jeremiah prophesy?

_____ b. What did Zedekiah do to Jeremiah?

Jeremiah 38

_____ a. What do the princes do to Jeremiah?

_____ b. What did Jeremiah do for Zedekiah?

Jeremiah 39

_____ a. What happened to Jerusalem and its people?

_____ b. Who were preserved?

Jeremiah 40

_____ a. What was Gedaliah assigned to be?

_____ b. What happened to Jeremiah?

Jeremiah 41

_____ a. What did Ishmael do?

Jeremiah 42

_____ a. What did Jeremiah promise Johanan if the remnant of the Jews remained in Judah?

_____ b. What did Jeremiah promise Johanan if they went to Egypt?

Jeremiah 43

_____ a. What did Johanan do?

_____ b. What did Jeremiah prophesy about Egypt?

Jeremiah 44

_____ a. What did Jeremiah prophesy would happen to most of the Jews in Egypt? Why?

Jeremiah 45

_____ a. What did Jeremiah promise Baruch?

Jeremiah 46

_____ a. What did Jeremiah prophesy about Egypt?

_____ b. What would happen to Jacob?

Jeremiah 47

_____ a. What did Jeremiah prophesy about the Philistines?

Jeremiah 48

_____ a. What would happen to Moab? Why?

Jeremiah 49

_____ a. What would happen to other nations?

Jeremiah 50

_____ a. What would happen to Babylon?

_____ b. What would happen to scattered Israel?

Jeremiah 51

VERSE NUMBER

_____ a. What would come upon Babylon? Why?

_____ b. What was Israel commanded to do?

Jeremiah 52

VERSE NUMBER

_____ a. What happened to Jerusalem?

_____ b. What happened to the people and to the vessels of the Lord's house?

The LAMENTATIONS of Jeremiah

Introduction

See Bible Dictionary, page 722, s.v. "Lamentations, Book of."

_____ a. What is being lamented?

_____ b. Who wrote the lamentations?

_____ c. What kind of poems are the lamentations?

_____ d. List four things we learn from this book.

Lamentations 1

VERSE NUMBER

_____ a. What did Jeremiah lament?

_____ b. What did Jerusalem complain of?

Lamentations 2

VERSE NUMBER

_____ a. What prevailed in Jerusalem?

Lamentations 3

VERSE NUMBER

_____ a. What did Jeremiah do?

Lamentations 4

VERSE NUMBER

_____ a. Why was the state of Zion pitiful?

Lamentations 5

VERSE NUMBER

_____ a. What did Jeremiah recite in prayer?

The Book of the Prophet EZEKIEL

Introduction

See Bible Dictionary, page 668, s.v. "Ezekiel."

_____ a. What does *Ezekiel* mean?

_____ b. Who was Ezekiel?

_____ c. When did he prophesy?

_____ d. What are the three main divisions of his book?

_____ e. List three notable teachings of Ezekiel.

_____ f. What did Ezekiel speak often about?

Ezekiel 1

_____ a. List three things that Ezekiel saw in his vision.

Ezekiel 2

_____ a. What was Ezekiel called to do?

_____ b. What was written in the book he saw?

Ezekiel 3

_____ a. What did the Lord make Ezekiel to be?

_____ b. What would happen to Ezekiel if he failed to warn the people?

Ezekiel 4

_____ a. What did Ezekiel create?

Ezekiel 5

_____ a. List four things the judgment of Jerusalem would include.

Ezekiel 6

_____ a. Why would Israel be destroyed?

_____ b. What would happen to a remnant of Israel?

Ezekiel 7

_____ a. What would sweep the land of Israel?

Ezekiel 8

_____ a. List two things Ezekiel saw in his vision.

Ezekiel 9

_____ a. What did Ezekiel see concerning the righteous and the wicked?

Ezekiel 10

_____ a. What did Ezekiel see in his vision?

Ezekiel 11

_____ a. What did Ezekiel see in vision about Jerusalem and the Jews?

_____ b. What did he prophesy about Israel?

Ezekiel 12

_____ a. Where were the Jews to be scattered?

Ezekiel 13

_____ a. Whom did Ezekiel reprove? Why?

Ezekiel 14

_____ a. Whom did the Lord refuse to answer?

_____ b. What did Ezekiel cry to the people?

Ezekiel 15

VERSE NUMBER

_____ a. What would happen to Jerusalem?

Ezekiel 16

VERSE NUMBER

_____ a. Whom had Jerusalem become like?

_____ b. What had Jerusalem done?

_____ c. What would the Lord do with Jerusalem in the last days?

Ezekiel 17

VERSE NUMBER

_____ a. What did Ezekiel show in a parable?

Ezekiel 18

VERSE NUMBER

_____ a. What will men be punished for?

_____ b. Who will save their souls?

_____ c. Who will be damned?

_____ d. Who will be saved?

Ezekiel 19

VERSE NUMBER

_____ a. Why did Ezekiel lament for Israel?

Ezekiel 20

VERSE NUMBER

_____ a. How long had Israel rebelled and failed to keep the commandments?

_____ b. What would the Lord do in the last days?

201

Ezekiel 21

_____ a. Who in Jerusalem would be slain?

_____ b. What would Babylon do?

Ezekiel 22

_____ a. What did Ezekiel catalog?

_____ b. Why would the Jews be scattered and destroyed?

Ezekiel 23

_____ a. Who were the two sisters?

_____ b. What did they do?

_____ c. What happened to them?

Ezekiel 24

_____ a. What is foretold in Ezekiel 24?

_____ b. What sign did Ezekiel give to the Jews?

Ezekiel 25

_____ a. Upon whom would the Lord's vengeance fall?

Ezekiel 26

_____ a. Why would Tyrus be destroyed?

Ezekiel 27

_____ a. What did Ezekiel lament?

Ezekiel 28

_____ a. Who would fall and be destroyed?

_____ b. What would happen to Israel?

Ezekiel 29

_____ a. Who would overthrow Egypt?

_____ b. What would Egypt be when she rises again?

Ezekiel 30

_____ a. Who would be made desolate by Babylon?

Ezekiel 31

_____ a. What was compared to the glory and fall of the Assyrians?

Ezekiel 32

_____ a. What did Ezekiel lament for?

Ezekiel 33

_____ a. Who would save their souls?

_____ b. Who else are saved?

_____ c. Who are damned?

_____ d. Why would the Jews be destroyed?

Ezekiel 34

_____ a. Whom did the Lord reprove?

_____ b. What three things would the Lord do in the last days?

Ezekiel 35

_____ a. Upon whom will the judgment fall? Why? (See also Bible Dictionary, p. 706, s.v. "Idumea.")

Ezekiel 36

_____ a. What would happen to the house of Israel in the last days?

_____ b. What would the Lord give them?

Ezekiel 37

_____ a. What would Israel inherit? When?

_____ b. What would become one in the Lord's hand?

_____ c. What would happen to Israel?

_____ d. What would they receive?

Ezekiel 38

_____ a. What will usher in the Second Coming? (See also D&C 29:21.)

_____ b. What will the earth be like when the Lord comes?

_____ c. What will men do at his presence?

Ezekiel 39

_____ a. Who will be destroyed?

_____ b. How long will it take to burn the weapons of war?

_____ c. How long will it take to bury the dead?

_____ d. What will happen after that?

Ezekiel 40

_____ a. What was Ezekiel shown in vision?

Ezekiel 41

_____ a. What was Ezekiel shown?

Ezekiel 42

_____ a. What did Ezekiel see?

Ezekiel 43

_____ a. What fills the temple?

_____ b. What is in the temple?

_____ c. What did the Lord promise to do?

Ezekiel 44

_____ a. What filled the house of the Lord?

_____ b. Who may not enter the sanctuary?

_____ c. What services are set forth?

Ezekiel 45

_____ a. For whom would land be provided?

_____ b. What are the people to do?

Ezekiel 46

_____ a. What ordinances are set forth?

Ezekiel 47

_____ a. How would the Dead Sea be healed?

_____ b. What did the Lord show Ezekiel?

Ezekiel 48

_____ a. How would the gates of the city be named?

_____ b. What would be the name of the city?

The Book of DANIEL

Introduction

See Bible Dictionary, page 653, s.v. "Daniel, Book of."

_____ a. What are the two main divisions of the book of Daniel?

_____ b. What does the book teach?

_____ c. What is the major contribution of the book?

_____ d. List four other significant items in the book.

_____ e. How were Daniel and his friends protected? Why?

_____ f. What gift did Daniel have that Joseph who was sold into Egypt also had?

Daniel 1

_____ a. What children were to be brought to the king's court? Why?

_____ b. What food did Daniel ask for? (See also Daniel 1:12a.)

_____ c. What did God give the four children?

_____ d. What did the king find when he interviewed them?

Daniel 2

_____ a. What did the dreams of King Nebuchadnezzar do to him?

_____ b. How did Daniel know the interpretation of the king's dream?

_____ c. What did Daniel say to the king before telling him of his dream?

_____ d. What was the interpretation of the dream?

_____ e. What is the stone? (See D&C 65:2.)

_____ f. What did the king do for Daniel? (See also Daniel 2:49b.)

Daniel 3

_____ a. Why were the people gathered to the plain of Dura?

_____ b. What would happen to those who did not worship the idol?

_____ c. Why were Shadrach, Meshach, and Abed-nego called before Nebuchadnezzar?

_____ d. How did they answer the king?

_____ e. Who was slain by the fire?

_____ f. What did the king see in the fire?

_____ g. What did the king's host observe about Shadrach, Meshach, and Abed-nego?

_____ h. What did Nebuchadnezzar decree?

Daniel 4

_____ a. Whom did Nebuchadnezzar gather to interpret his dream?

_____ b. Describe the king's dream.

_____ c. What was the purpose of the dream?

_____ d. What was the interpretation of the dream?

_____ e. What counsel did Daniel give the king? (See also Mosiah 4:21; D&C 42:31.)

_____ f. What message was given the king from heaven?

_____ g. What happened to Nebuchadnezzar for seven years?

_____ h. What happened to Nebuchadnezzar at the end of seven years? (See also Daniel 4:34a.)

_____ i. Whom did Nebuchadnezzar "praise and extol and honour"? (V. 37.)

Daniel 5

_____ a. What did King Belshazzar do to offend God?

_____ b. What happened "in the same hour"? (Daniel 5:5.)

_____ c. What did the queen say to the king to recommend Daniel?

_____ d. What did the king promise Daniel if he would interpret the writing?

_____ e. How did Daniel respond?

_____ f. When did Nebuchadnezzar lose his throne and his glory?

_____ g. What had Belshazzar failed to do?

_____ h. What was the interpretation of the writing on the wall?

_____ i. What happened to Belshazzar that night?

_____ j. Who took the kingdom?

Daniel 6

_____ a. What position did King Darius give Daniel?

_____ b. Why did the king seek "to set him over the whole realm"? (Daniel 6:3.)

_____ c. How did the "presidents and princes" seek to destroy Daniel? (V. 4.)

_____ d. What did Daniel do when the decree was signed?

_____ e. How did the king feel when Daniel disobeyed the decree?

_____ f. What did the king say to Daniel before he was cast into the den of lions?

_____ g. What did the king do while Daniel was in the lion's den?

_____ h. How was Daniel saved?

_____ i. What decree did Darius send throughout his kingdom?

Daniel 7

_____ a. Describe the four beasts in Daniel's dream.

_____ b. Who is the "Ancient of days"? (See Daniel 7:9c.)

_____ c. What will happen at the Second Coming?

_____ d. What do the four beasts represent?

_____ e. Who shall take the kingdom and possess it?

_____ f. What "made war with the saints, and prevailed against them"? (V. 21; see also D&C 29:21.)

_____ g. What did the fourth beast and its horns represent?

h. What will happen to the kingdom of the fourth beast?

Daniel 8

_____ a. Which kingdoms are represented by the ram and the goat?

_____ b. What will the fierce king do in the latter days?

_____ c. When will he be destroyed?

Daniel 9

_____ a. What did Daniel do before God?

_____ b. What did Gabriel reveal to Daniel? Why?

Daniel 10

_____ a. Whom did Daniel see in vision?

_____ b. How did Daniel describe the Lord? (See also Ezekiel 1:26–28; Revelation 1:13–15; D&C 110: 2–3.)

_____ c. What did those who were with Daniel do when he saw his vision?

Daniel 11

_____ a. What did Daniel see in his vision?

Daniel 12

_____ a. What will Michael do in the last days?

_____ b. What did Daniel tell of?

_____ c. What will the wise know?

HOSEA

Introduction

See Bible Dictionary, page 705, s.v. "Hosea."

_____ a. Who was Hosea?

_____ b. When did Hosea live?

_____ c. What was happening in Israel when Hosea lived?

_____ d. What is Hosea's fundamental theme?

_____ e. List four ways God has shown his love for his people.

_____ f. How has Israel responded to God's love?

Hosea 1

VERSE NUMBER

_____ a. Who were to be a sign to Israel?

_____ b. What would Israel be in the days of gathering?

Hosea 2

VERSE NUMBER

_____ a. What has brought severe judgments upon Israel?

_____ b. What would happen to Israel in the last days?

Hosea 3

_____ a. List three things Israel would do in the last days.

Hosea 4

_____ a. What did Israel lose?

Hosea 5

_____ a. What would happen to the kingdoms of Judah and Israel? Why?

Hosea 6

_____ a. What did Hosea call Israel to do?

_____ b. What is more important to the Lord than sacrifices?

Hosea 7

_____ a. Why was Israel reproved?

_____ b. What happened to Ephraim?

Hosea 8

_____ a. Who had forsaken the Lord?

_____ b. What had the Lord written to Ephraim?

Hosea 9

_____ a. What happened to the children of Israel for their sins?

_____ b. What happened to Ephraim?

Hosea 10

_____ a. What had Israel done?

_____ b. What did Hosea call upon them to do?

Hosea 11

_____ a. What was Israel's coming out of Egypt in similitude of?

_____ b. What did Ephraim do?

Hosea 12

_____ a. List three ways the Lord guides his people.

_____ b. What did the Lord's people fail to do when they became rich?

_____ c. What did Ephraim do?

Hosea 13

_____ a. What provoked the Lord?

_____ b. What did the Savior do?

Hosea 14

_____ a. What would Ephraim do in the last days?

JOEL

Introduction

See Bible Dictionary, page 714, s.v. "Joel."

_____ a. Who was Joel?

_____ b. What prompted Joel's prophecy?

_____ c. What did Joel assure the people?

_____ d. Who quoted in other scripture Joel's "prophecy of the outpouring of the Spirit"?

Joel 1

_____ a. What did the Lord instruct Joel to do?

Joel 2

_____ a. List four things that will precede the Second Coming. (See also Joseph Smith–History 1:41.)

Joel 3

_____ a. What will all nations be doing?

_____ b. Where will the multitudes stand?

_____ c. Where will the Lord dwell?

AMOS

Introduction

See Bible Dictionary, page 607, s.v. "Amos."

_____ a. When did Amos prophesy?

_____ b. Who was Amos?

_____ c. What did Amos emphasize?

_____ d. List five things the book of Amos shows.

Amos 1

_____ a. What did Amos show in Amos 1?

Amos 2

_____ a. On whom would the Lord pour out his judgments? Why?

Amos 3

_____ a. To whom does the Lord reveal his secrets?

_____ b. Why was Israel overwhelmed by an adversary?

Amos 4

_____ a. What judgments did the Lord send upon his people?

_____ b. How did the people respond?

Amos 5

_____ a. What was Israel encouraged to do?

_____ b. How did they offend the Lord?

Amos 6

_____ a. What would happen to those who are at ease in Zion and to Israel?

Amos 7

_____ a. What did Amos prophesy?

Amos 8

_____ a. What would there be a famine of?

Amos 9

_____ a. What would happen soon to Israel?

_____ b. What would happen to Israel in the last days?

OBADIAH

Introduction

See Bible Dictionary, page 739, s.v. "Obadiah (2)."

_____ a. What did Obadiah foretell?

_____ b. What is one of the better known passages in the book? Why?

Obadiah 1

_____ a. What did Obadiah prophesy?

_____ b. Who would stand upon Mount Zion? (See Obadiah 1:21*a*.)

JONAH

Introduction

See Bible Dictionary, page 716, s.v. "Jonah."

_____ a. What does the book of Jonah describe?

_____ b. What is the key to the book?

_____ c. What did the writer oppose?

_____ d. What did the writer show?

_____ e. When did the Lord refer to the prophet Jonah? Why?

Jonah 1

VERSE NUMBER

_____ a. What was Jonah sent to do?

_____ b. What happened to Jonah when he fled by ship?

Jonah 2

VERSE NUMBER

_____ a. What happened when Jonah prayed to the Lord?

Jonah 3

VERSE NUMBER

_____ a. What did Jonah prophesy?

_____ b. Why was the city saved?

Jonah 4

VERSE NUMBER

_____ a. Why was Jonah displeased with the Lord?

_____ b. What did the Lord do?

MICAH

Introduction

See Bible Dictionary, page 731, s.v. "Micah."

_____ a. Under whom did Micah prophesy?

_____ b. Describe the three divisions of the book.

_____ c. What does the last chapter of Micah contain?

Micah 1

_____ a. What did Micah prophesy?

Micah 2

_____ a. What was lamented?

_____ b. What would the Lord gather?

Micah 3

_____ a. Who brings a curse on the people?

Micah 4

_____ a. List four events of the last days.

Micah 5

_____ a. Where would the Messiah be born?

_____ b. Who would triumph over the gentiles in the last days?

Micah 6

_____ a. What have the people failed to do?

b. What must they do?

Micah 7

_____ a. What would the Lord do for Israel in the last days?

NAHUM

Introduction

See Bible Dictionary, page 736, s.v. "Nahum."

_____ a. Against whom did Nahum prophesy?

_____ b. What are his themes?

_____ c. What does the prophecy have in it?

_____ d. When was the prophecy probably written?

Nahum 1

_____ a. What did Nahum speak of?

Nahum 2

_____ a. What would happen to Nineveh?

_____ b. What is this destruction a type of?

Nahum 3

_____ a. What was foretold?

HABAKKUK

Introduction

See Bible Dictionary, page 697, s.v. "Habakkuk."

_____ a. Approximately when did Habakkuk prophesy?

_____ b. What are his themes?

Habakkuk 1

VERSE NUMBER

_____ a. Why was Habakkuk troubled?

Habakkuk 2

VERSE NUMBER

_____ a. What did the Lord promise?

_____ b. What would happen to the earth?

Habakkuk 3

VERSE NUMBER

_____ a. Why did Habakkuk tremble in his prayer?

ZEPHANIAH

Introduction

See Bible Dictionary, page 792, s.v. "Zephaniah."

_____ a. When did Zephaniah prophesy?

_____ b. What did he speak about in his prophecy?

_____ c. What is the "day of the Lord"?

_____ d. Upon whom do the Lord's judgments fall?

Zephaniah 1

_____ a. What is a type of the Second Coming?

_____ b. What will the Second Coming be a day of?

Zephaniah 2

_____ a. What should we seek?

Zephaniah 3

_____ a. Why will all nations assemble at the Second Coming?

_____ b. Why will people have a pure language?

_____ c. How will the Lord reign in their midst?

HAGGAI

Introduction

See Bible Dictionary, page 698, s.v. "Haggai."

_____ a. When was Haggai's prophecy spoken?

_____ b. What did his prophecy encourage the people to do?

_____ c. What did his preaching produce?

_____ d. How did Haggai speak in chapter 2?

_____ e. What warning did he give the people?

_____ f. Why did he look to the future in hope?

Haggai 1

_____ a. What did Haggai exhort the people to do?

Haggai 2

_____ a. Where would peace be found?

ZECHARIAH

Introduction

See Bible Dictionary, page 791, s.v. "Zechariah."

_____ a. When did Zechariah prophesy?

_____ b. Describe the two divisions in the book.

_____ c. What are the eight visions in chapters 1 through 6?

_____ d. What are the two themes of chapters 9 through 11?

_____ e. What are the two themes of chapters 12 through 14?

Zechariah 1

_____ a. What did Zechariah call upon Judah to do?

_____ b. What was he shown by visions?

Zechariah 2

_____ a. Where would Judah gather to in the last days?

_____ b. Where would they come from?

_____ c. Who would dwell with them?

Zechariah 3

_____ a. What would happen at the Second Coming?

Zechariah 4

_____ a. What would Zerubbabel do?

Zechariah 5

_____ a. How did the angel reveal truths to Zechariah?

Zechariah 6

_____ a. Whom did Zechariah crown?

_____ b. What will Christ be?

Zechariah 7

_____ a. What did the Lord reprove?

_____ b. What did he call the people to do?

Zechariah 8

_____ a. List three events that would occur in the last days.

Zechariah 9

_____ a. What would the Messiah do when he came?

Zechariah 10

_____ a. What would happen to the descendants of Judah and of Joseph?

_____ b. What would the Lord do for them?

Zechariah 11

_____ a. For what would the Messiah be betrayed?

_____ b. What would happen to it?

Zechariah 12

_____ a. Where would the final great war be fought? (See also Bible Dictionary, p. 614, s.v. "Armageddon.")

_____ b. Who would defend Judah?

_____ c. What would the Jews do?

Zechariah 13

_____ a. What will the Jews obtain at the Second Coming?

_____ b. What will the Jews ask Jesus at his second coming?

_____ c. Who shall be his people?

Zechariah 14

_____ a. What will the Lord do at his second coming?

_____ b. Where will he stand?

_____ c. Who shall be king over all the earth?

_____ d. What will destroy the wicked?

MALACHI

Introduction

See Bible Dictionary, page 728, s.v. "Malachi."

_____ a. When was the prophecy of Malachi given?

_____ b. Describe the two parts of the prophecy.

_____ c. What are the faithful encouraged to do?

_____ d. Describe four notable passages.

Malachi 1

_____ a. How did the Jews despise the Lord?

_____ b. Among whom would the Lord's name be great?

Malachi 2

_____ a. Why were the priests reproved?

_____ b. Why were the Jews condemned?

Malachi 3

_____ a. What would the Lord's messenger do?

_____ b. What was Israel commanded to do?

_____ c. Whose names will be found in the book of remembrance?

Malachi 4

_____ a. What will happen to the proud and the wicked at the Second Coming?

_____ b. When will Elijah return? (See D&C 110:13–16.)

Questions about the Pearl of Great Price

Selections from the Book of MOSES

Introduction

See Bible Dictionary, page 734, s.v. "Moses."

_____ a. Upon whom did Moses and Elijah bestow the keys of the priesthood on the Mount of Transfiguration?

_____ b. Why did Moses have a body of flesh and bone at the time of the transfiguration?

_____ c. What keys did Moses confer upon Joseph Smith and Oliver Cowdery in the Kirtland Temple?

_____ d. What does latter-day revelation confirm about Moses?

_____ e. Why is Moses 1 "of exceptional worth" to the study of Genesis? (See Introductory Note to the Pearl of Great Price; Bible Dictionary, p. 678, s.v. "Genesis.")

_____ f. List three contributions the book of Moses makes to our study of the book of Genesis. (See Bible Dictionary, p. 678, s.v. "Genesis.")

Moses 1

VERSE NUMBER

_____ a. Where did the Lord speak to Moses? (See also Moses 1:42.)

_____ b. How was Moses able to talk with the Lord face to face?

_____ c. Why did the Lord refrain from showing Moses all his works?

_____ d. What did the Lord show Moses?

_____ e. What did Satan want Moses to do?

_____ f. What did Moses say to Satan?

_____ g. What did Satan do when Moses refused to follow him?

_____ h. What blessings did Moses receive after rejecting Satan?

_____ i. Who created the "worlds without number" that Moses saw? (V. 33.)

_____ j. What is the work and glory of God?

_____ k. To whom would this record be shown?

Moses 2

_____ a. What did God do on each day of the creation?

_____ Day 1

_____ Day 2 (See also Moses 2:8a.)

_____ Day 3 (See also v. 10a.)

_____ Day 4

_____ Day 5

_____ Day 6

_____ Day 7 (See Moses 3:2–4.)

Moses 3

_____ a. Why has God blessed and sanctified the seventh day?

_____ b. How were all things created "before they were naturally upon the face of the earth"? (Moses 3:5.)

_____ c. Who was the first flesh upon the earth?

_____ d. Where did God put the man He had formed?

_____ e. What two trees were also planted in the Garden?

_____ f. Where was Eden? (See Bible Dictionary, p. 659, s.v. "Eden, Garden of.")

_____ g. What tree was Adam forbidden to eat the fruit of? Why?

_____ h. Who named all the animals?

_____ i. Why should a man leave his father and mother?

Moses 4

VERSE NUMBER

_____ a. What did Satan say to the Father?

_____ b. What did Jesus say to the Father?

_____ c. Why was Satan cast down?

_____ d. What will Satan do to those who will not obey God?

_____ e. Why did Satan seek to beguile Eve?

_____ f. What happened to the eyes of Adam and Eve when they ate of the fruit?

_____ g. What did God say to Eve about her children and husband?

_____ h. What did God say to Adam?

_____ i. Why were Adam and Eve sent out of the Garden?

Moses 5

VERSE NUMBER

_____ a. Why were Adam and Eve unable to see the Lord?

_____ b. What did the Lord command Adam and Eve to do?

_____ c. Why did Adam offer sacrifices unto the Lord?

_____ d. Why were Adam and Eve commanded to offer sacrifices unto the Lord?

_____ e. Why did Adam and Eve bless the name of God?

_____ f. What do people become when they love Satan more than God?

_____ g. What did the Lord do by the Holy Ghost?

_____ h. What did Satan command Cain to do?

_____ i. What did the Lord say to Cain about his offering? Why?

_____ j. How did Cain respond?

_____ k. Whom did Cain marry?

_____ l. Why did Cain call himself Master Mahan? (See also Moses 5:31d.)

_____ m. What did Cain do and say after killing Abel?

_____ n. How was Cain punished for killing Abel?

_____ o. Why did Lamech kill Irad?

_____ p. Why was Lamech afraid to come among the sons of men?

_____ q. How was the gospel preached?

Moses 6

_____ a. To whom did God reveal himself?

_____ b. What book did Adam's posterity keep?

_____ c. Who wrote "by the spirit of inspiration"? (Moses 6:5.)

_____ d. For how many years did Adam live?

_____ e. What caused the "wars and bloodshed"? (V. 15.)

_____ f. What did Seth, Enos, Cainan, Mahalaleel, Jared, and Enoch do in their days?

_____ g. What was Enoch called of the Lord to do? Why?

_____ h. What did Enoch say to the Lord?

_____ i. What did the Lord tell Enoch to do?

_____ j. Why was Enoch called a seer?

_____ k. Why did the people refrain from laying their hands upon Enoch?

_____ l. What has God made known to our fathers?

_____ m. What was required of Adam to receive the Holy Ghost?

_____ n. What was Adam commanded to teach his children? Why?

_____ o. How are we justified and sanctified?

_____ p. How was Adam baptized?

VERSE NUMBER

_____ a. What happened to Adam's children who believed? who did not believe?

_____ b. What happened to Enoch as he "stood upon the mount"? (Moses 7:3.)

_____ c. How did Enoch converse with the Lord? (See also Moses 1:11.)

_____ d. What did Enoch prophesy would happen to the children of Canaan?

_____ e. What was Enoch able to do because of his faith?

_____ f. What did the Lord call his people? Why?

_____ g. What was the name of the city that Enoch built?

_____ h. When Enoch saw the earth after "Zion was taken up into heaven" (Moses 7:23), what were the angels of God doing? what were Satan and his angels doing?

_____ i. What happened to those upon whom the Holy Ghost fell?

_____ j. Why will the heavens weep?

_____ k. How wicked were the people?

_____ l. Why did Enoch weep over his brethren?

_____ m. In verse 47, what event did Enoch see?

_____ n. What did the "voice from the bowels" of the earth say to Enoch? (V. 48.)

_____ o. What did the Lord covenant with Enoch?

_____ p. What will happen to the earth before it is able to rest?

_____ q. What would be the name of the gathering place in the last days?

_____ r. Who would meet at the gathering place?

_____ s. What did the Lord show Enoch would happen before the Second Coming?

_____ t. What happened to the city that Enoch had built?

Moses 8

_____ a. Why was Methuselah not taken with his father, Enoch?

_____ b. Why did many people die in the days of Methuselah?

_____ c. How old was Methuselah when he died?

_____ d. Why were Noah and his sons called the sons of God?

_____ e. Why were the giants unable to kill Noah?

_____ f. What did the Lord command Noah to do?

_____ g. What kind of thoughts were continually in each man's heart?

_____ h. What message did Noah continue to deliver?

_____ i. What kind of men were Noah and his sons?

_____ j. What was the earth filled with before the Flood?

The Book of ABRAHAM

Introduction

See Bible Dictionary, page 601, s.v. "Abraham."

_____ a. What does _Abraham_ mean?

_____ b. What does _Abram_ mean? (See also Genesis 17:5.)

_____ c. Who is "regarded in the Old Testament as founder of the covenant race"?

_____ d. What knowledge was Abraham blessed with through divine revelation?

_____ e. When was Abraham "chosen to be a leader in the kingdom of God"? Why?

_____ f. Because of his faithfulness, where is Abraham now? (See D&C 132:29, 37.)

See Bible Dictionary, page 602, s.v. "Abraham, covenant of."

_____ g. What covenant is made at the time of baptism?

_____ h. What covenant is made at the time of temple marriage?

_____ i. After Abraham made these two covenants, what promise did he receive?

_____ j. List three parts of the Abrahamic covenant.

_____ k. What part of this covenant is renewed with those who enter celestial marriage?

_____ l. How do the gentiles become heirs of the covenant?

_____ m. What are the heirs of the covenant chosen to do?

_____ n. List five things that must take place in the last days to fulfill the covenant that the Lord made with Abraham.

Abraham 1

_____ a. What record was this book translated from?

_____ b. For what did Abraham seek? Why?

_____ c. Why did Abraham's fathers refuse to heed his message?

_____ d. What did the Lord say to Abraham when he was about to be sacrificed?

_____ e. What would happen as a result of Abraham's ministry?

_____ f. What happened to the priests who were about to kill Abraham?

_____ g. Who established the first government in Egypt?

_____ h. What type of government was it?

_____ i. What did Pharaoh seek earnestly to do?

_____ j. How was Pharaoh blessed by Noah?

_____ k. How was Pharaoh cursed by Noah? Why?

_____ l. What began to be fulfilled at the time of the death of the priest of Elkanah?

_____ m. What was contained in the records Abraham had?

Abraham 2

_____ a. Why did Abraham leave the land of Ur of the Chaldees?

_____ b. Who went with him?

_____ c. How were Abraham and his seed to be blessed?

_____ d. What did Abraham say in his heart?

_____ e. For what did Abraham pray in the land of Jershon?

_____ f. What did the Lord tell Abraham when he entered the land of Canaan?

_____ g. Why did Abraham "go down into Egypt"? (Abraham 2:21.)

_____ h. Why could Abraham tell the Egyptians that Sarah was his sister?

Abraham 3

_____ a. What had the Lord given Abraham in Ur of the Chaldees?

_____ b. What has the Lord set Kolob to do?

_____ c. How many earth years are equal to one day to the Lord?

_____ d. How did Abraham talk with the Lord?

_____ e. In verse 11, what did the Lord tell Abraham?

_____ f. What did the Lord tell Abraham about his descendants?

_____ g. What does the Lord do about what he takes "in his heart to do"? (Abraham 3:17.)

_____ h. In verse 19, what did the Lord tell Abraham?

_____ i. What was Abraham shown?

_____ j. What will God do with "the noble and great ones"? (V. 22.)

_____ k. Why was the earth prepared for us? (See also D&C 132:37.)

_____ l. What will happen to those who keep their second estate (life on earth)?

_____ m. Who did not keep their first estate (premortal life in the spirit world)?

Abraham 4

_____ a. What did the Gods do on each day of the creation?

_____ Day 1

_____ Day 2

_____ Day 3

_____ Day 4

_____ Day 5

_____ Day 6

_____ Day 7 (See Abraham 5:1–3.)

Abraham 5

_____ a. What trees were planted in the Garden of Eden?

_____ b. What was Adam to do in the Garden?

_____ c. Why did people not live to be one thousand years old? (See Abraham 3:4.)

_____ d. Why was a woman made for Adam?

_____ e. To whom did Adam give names?

Answers

Title Page
a. page i
b. page i

"To the Most High and Mighty Prince James . . . ": The Epistle Dedicatory
a. page iii
b. pages iii–iv

The Names and Order of All the Books of the Old and New Testament
a. page v
b. page v
c. page v

Explanation Concerning Abbreviations
a. page vi
b. page vi
c. page vi
d. page vi
e. page vi
f. page vi
g. page vi

Historical Background
Bible Dictionary

Genesis

Introduction
Bible Dictionary

Genesis 1
a. 1:1–31; 2:1–3

Genesis 2
a. Moses 3:5
b. 9
c. 17
d. 19–20
e. 23

Genesis 3
a. 1–5
b. 7–10
c. 14–15
d. 16
e. 17–19
f. 20
g. 22–24

Genesis 4
a. 3
b. 4
c. 5
d. 9
e. 10–15
f. 25

Genesis 5
a. 2
b. 21
c. 24
d. 25–26
e. 27
f. 28–30
g. 32, Bible Dictionary

Genesis 6
a. 5
b. 6–7
c. 11–13
d. 14
e. 18–20
f. 22

Genesis 7
a. 1, 4
b. 2–3
c. 4, 12
d. 7, 13
e. 21–23
f. 24

Genesis 8
a. 8–13
b. 15–16
c. 20
d. JST Genesis 9:4–6

Genesis 9
a. 1
b. 3
c. JST Genesis 9:10
d. JST Genesis 9:11
e. JST Genesis 9:12–13
f. 9–11
g. 9a; JST Genesis 9:21–23
h. 12–17
i. 18
j. 25–27

Genesis 10
a. 8–9
b. 25
c. 32

Genesis 11
a. Helaman 6:28
b. 6
c. 9
d. 10–27

Genesis 12
a. 1–3
b. 10
c. Abraham 2:22–24
d. 14–16
e. 17
f. 18–20

Genesis 13
a. 5–7
b. 8–9
c. 10–11
d. 13b
e. 14–17
f. 18

Genesis 14
a. 11–12
b. 16
c. 18–20, 18d
d. 20
e. 21–23
f. JST Genesis 14:30–31

Genesis 15
a. 2
b. JST Genesis 15:12
c. 13, 13a

Genesis 16
a. D&C 132:34–35
b. 4
c. 5
d. 6
e. 7–12
f. 11a

Genesis 17
a. 3–5
b. 6–8
c. 10–11
d. 15a
e. 16
f. 17, 17a
g. 19
h. 23

Genesis 18
a. 2–5
b. 9–10
c. 19
d. 22a
e. 32

Genesis 19
a. 1a
b. 2–3
c. 5, 5a
d. JST Genesis 19:13
e. 10–11
f. 13
g. 14
h. 24
i. 17, 26
j. 31–36, 35a

Genesis 20
a. 2
b. 4–7, 14
c. 12
d. 17–18

Genesis 21
a. 4
b. 9–10
c. 11–13
d. 14
e. 16–20
f. 21
g. 23
h. 28–30

Genesis 22
a. 1a
b. 2
c. 3
d. 10–13
e. 16–18

Genesis 23
a. 3–4, 8–9
b. 6, 10–11
c. 16–18

Genesis 24
a. 1–9
b. 12–14
c. 15–21
d. 24; Abraham 2:2
e. 29–33
f. 50–51
g. 60
h. 67

Genesis 25
a. 5
b. 6
c. 7
d. 9
e. 22–23
f. 28
g. 29–34

Genesis 26
a. 1–5
b. 7
c. 10–11
d. 12–14
e. 16
f. 17–18
g. 26–29

Genesis 27
a. 3–4
b. 8–10
c. 27–29

d. 36a
e. 38–40
f. 41
g. 43

Genesis 28
a. 1–4
b. 2
c. 12–15
d. 20–22

Genesis 29
a. 9–10
b. 13–14
c. 18
d. 25–26
e. 18, 20, 27, 30
f. 31–35

Genesis 30
a. 1
b. 3
c. Bible Dictionary
d. 24
e. 27
f. 28–34
g. 37–42

Genesis 31
a. 3
b. 6–9
c. 14–16
d. 19
e. 26–30
f. 49–53

Genesis 32
a. 1
b. 3–5
c. 7–12
d. 16–20
e. 26–28
f. 30

Genesis 33
a. 4–5
b. 10–11
c. 12–14
d. 17

Genesis 34
a. 1–2
b. 13–17
c. 25–29

d. 30

Genesis 35
a. 1
b. 2–3
c. 5
d. 9–12
e. 16–19
f. 29

Genesis 36
a. 1

Genesis 37
a. 3
b. 4–5
c. 6–9
d. 21
e. 23–28
f. 31–33
g. 36

Genesis 38
a. 7
b. 11, 14, 26

Genesis 39
a. 3
b. 5
c. 6
d. 10
e. 11–12
f. 16–18
g. 21–23

Genesis 40
a. 1–3
b. 12–13
c. 14
d. 18–19

Genesis 41
a. 1–7
b. 8
c. 12–15
d. 16
e. 25–32
f. 33–36
g. 38–39
h. 40–41
i. 50–52
j. 54–57

Genesis 42
a. 1–2

b. 4
c. 7, 23, 30
d. 19–20
e. 21–22, 25–28
f. 38

Genesis 43
a. 4–5
b. 11–13
c. 16–17
d. 30
e. 32

Genesis 44
a. 1–2
b. 12–14
c. 16, 18–34

Genesis 45
a. 1–5
b. 3
c. 5–8
d. 9–13
e. 16
f. 17–20
g. 26–28

Genesis 46
a. 1–4
b. 27
c. 29
d. 31–34

Genesis 47
a. 2–4
b. 5–6
c. 7, 10
d. 6, 11
e. 14–20
f. 24, 26
g. 29–31

Genesis 48
a. JST Genesis 48:5–6
b. JST Genesis 48:7–11
c. 21–22

Genesis 49
a. 1–28, headnote
b. 10, headnote
c. Headnote
d. 24–26, headnote

Genesis 50
a. 3

b. 4–5
c. 7–9
d. 19–21
e. JST Genesis 50:
  24, 29, 34–35
f. JST Genesis
  50:25–30, 32–33
g. JST Genesis 50:31
h. JST Genesis 50:38

Exodus

Introduction
Bible Dictionary

Exodus 1
a. 7
b. 8–11
c. 17
d. 22

Exodus 2
a. 2–4
b. 5–6
c. 6
d. 7–9
e. 11–12
f. 13–15
g. 16–19
h. 23

Exodus 3
a. 2a, 6
b. 10
c. 14–18
d. 20
e. 21–22

Exodus 4
a. 1–9
b. 10
c. 14–16
d. 20
e. 21c
f. 22–23
g. JST Exodus 4:24
h. 29
i. 30
j. 31

Exodus 5
a. 1, 3
b. 2, 4–5

c. 6–14
d. 22–23

Exodus 6
a. 1–8
b. 3, 3c
c. 6–9
d. 9
e. 29–30, 30a

Exodus 7
a. 1b, c
b. 3a
c. 4–5
d. 7
e. 10–12
f. 13a
g. 17–21
h. 22

Exodus 8
a. 2–6
b. 7
c. 8
d. 15
e. 16–17
f. 18
g. 19
h. 21–24
i. 25, 32

Exodus 9
a. 3–6
b. 7
c. 8–10
d. 11
e. 12a
f. 18–26
g. 27–28, 34–35

Exodus 10
a. 4–6, 12–15
b. 16–17, 20a
c. 21–23
d. 24, 27a, 27–29

Exodus 11
a. 2
b. 4–7
c. 8

Exodus 12
a. 3–11
b. 5a

c. 11
d. 12–13
e. 17
f. 26–27
g. 29–30
h. 31–32
i. 37
j. 39
k. 40

Exodus 13
a. 1–2
b. 6–10
c. 14–15
d. 17
e. 19
f. 21–22

Exodus 14
a. 4–5
b. 10–12
c. 13–14
d. 19–20
e. 21
f. 22
g. 23–28
h. 28–31

Exodus 15
a. 18–19
b. 22–24
c. 25
d. 26

Exodus 16
a. 2–3
b. 4, 14–15
c. 13
d. 19–20
e. 22–28
f. 35

Exodus 17
a. 1–3
b. 5–6
c. 11–12

Exodus 18
a. 1
b. 2
c. 1–5
d. 7–8
e. 17–23
f. 21, 25

Exodus 19
a. 1–2
b. 3–6
c. 9
d. 11
e. 12–13
f. 20
g. 21–22

Exodus 20
a. 3–17
b. 18–19
c. 20
d. 24–26

Exodus 21
a. 10–11
b. 12–14
c. 15–17

Exodus 22
a. 1
b. 18, 18a
c. 20
d. 22–24

Exodus 23
a. 1–9
b. 10–11
c. 14–16
d. 20
e. 25–27
f. 27–30
g. 33

Exodus 24
a. 3
b. 9–11
c. 12
d. 18

Exodus 25
a. 1–7
b. 8–9
c. 21–22
d. Bible Dictionary

Exodus 26
a. 1, 26, headnote
b. 33, headnote
c. 34, headnote

Exodus 27
a. Headnote

b. 21, headnote

Exodus 28
a. 1
b. 4
c. 15–21, headnote
d. 30*a*
e. Bible Dictionary

Exodus 29
a. 1–9, 10–35, headnote
b. Headnote
c. 42–46, headnote

Exodus 30
a. 1, 6, headnote
b. 10, headnote
c. 12, 16, headnote
d. 18–38, headnote

Exodus 31
a. 1–11
b. 1–13, 16–17
c. 14–15
d. 18

Exodus 32
a. 1, 23
b. 4
c. 7–8
d. 11–13, 12*b*
e. JST Exodus 32:14
f.
g. 20
h. 26
i. 33
j. 35

Exodus 33
a. 2–4
b. 7
c. 8–10
d. 11
e. 16
f. JST Exodus 33:20

Exodus 34
a. 1–3
b. JST Exodus 34:1–2
c. 8–9
d. 12–17
e. 28
f. 29–30
g. 32–35

Exodus 35
a. 1–3
b. 5
c. 21–29
d. 25
e. 30–35

Exodus 36
a. 1–2
b. 5–7

Exodus 37
a. 1, 6–7, 10, 16–17, 25, 29, headnote

Exodus 38
a. Headnote

Exodus 39
a. 32–43, headnote

Exodus 40
a. 13–15, headnote
b. 33–34
c. 35
d. 36–37
e. 38

Leviticus

Introduction
    Bible Dictionary

Leviticus 1
a. 1
b. 3, headnote
c. 4, headnote
d. 5

Leviticus 2
a. Headnote
b. 1, 13
c. 3, 10
d. 11

Leviticus 3
a. 1–14, headnote
b. 2
c. 17, headnote

Leviticus 4
a. 2
b. 3, headnote

c. 35, headnote

Leviticus 5
a. 1, 5–6, headnote
b. 6–7, 10, 15–16, 19, headnote

Leviticus 6
a. 1–7, headnote
b. 12–13
c. 23, 30

Leviticus 7
a. 1, 11, 34, 37, headnote
b. 29, headnote
c. Headnote

Leviticus 8
a. 1–13, headnote
b. 14–30, 36, headnote

Leviticus 9
a. 8, headnote
b. 23, headnote
c. 24, headnote

Leviticus 10
a. 1
b. 2, headnote

Leviticus 11
a. 2–43, headnote
b. 44–45, headnote

Leviticus 12
a. 2–8, headnote
b. 2–5

Leviticus 13
a. Headnote
b. 45–46

Leviticus 14
a. Headnote

Leviticus 15
a. 1–33, headnote

Leviticus 16
a. 1–25, headnote
b. 17, 30, headnote
c. 29–34, headnote

Leviticus 17
a. 3–6, headnote
b. 11, headnote

Leviticus 18
a. 6–18, headnote
b. 20–23, headnote
c. 24–29, headnote

Leviticus 19
a. Headnote
b. 26–29, 31, 33, 35, headnote

Leviticus 20
a. 1–2, 9–13, 15–16, 27, headnote

Leviticus 21
a. 1–6, 10–12
b. 7–8, 13–14
c. 14, headnote

Leviticus 22
a. 3
b. 6–7
c. 21, headnote

Leviticus 23
a. 3, headnote
b. 5, 6, 10, 24, 27, 34, headnote

Leviticus 24
a. 2–4
b. 5–9, 5*a*
c. 14–16, headnote

Leviticus 25
a. 4, headnote
b. 10, headnote
c. Headnote
d. 36–37, headnote

Leviticus 26
a. 1–13, headnote
b. 14–39, headnote
c. 40–45, headnote

Leviticus 27
a. 30–34, headnote

Numbers

Introduction
    Bible Dictionary

Numbers 1
a. 3
b. 46–47
c. 52; 2:2

Numbers 2
a. 3–9
b. 10–16
c. 17
d. 18–24
e. 25–31

Numbers 3
a. 1–3, headnote
b. 6–7, headnote
c. 12, headnote

Numbers 4
a. 5–15, headnote
b. 1–4, 22–28, 29–33,
   35, headnote

Numbers 5
a. 6–7
b. 8
c. 11–31

Numbers 6
a. 1–21
b. 22–27

Numbers 7
a. 2–3, headnote
b. 5
c. 89, headnote

Numbers 8
a. 6–7, 10, headnote
b. 16–18
c. 11, 22–26, headnote

Numbers 9
a. 2–5, headnote
b. 13
c. 15, headnote
d. 17–22, headnote

Numbers 10
a. 2–10, headnote
b. 11–12, headnote
c. 29

Numbers 11
a. 1

b. 4–6
c. 11–15
d. 16–17
e. 18–20
f. 24–25
g. 31–33

Numbers 12
a. 26:59
b. 1–2
c. 3
d. 4–8
e. 10–15

Numbers 13
a. 2
b. 17–20
c. 27–29
d. 30
e. 28–31
f. 33

Numbers 14
a. 2–3
b. 6–9
c. 10
d. 13–20
e. 22–24
f. 33–34
g. 36–37
h. 40–45

Numbers 15
a. 30–31
b. 32–36

Numbers 16
a. 9–11
b. 27–33
c. 35
d. 41–50

Numbers 17
a. 1–5
b. 8
c. 10

Numbers 18
a. 1, headnote
b. 2–7, headnote
c. 8–19, 20–21, 24, 26–
   32, headnote

Numbers 19
a. 11, 16

b. 12–13, 20

Numbers 20
a. 1
b. 2–5
c. 8
d. 10–12, 12a
e. 18–21
f. 23–29

Numbers 21
a. 1–3
b. 4–5
c. 6
d. 8–9
e. Helaman 8:13–15
f. 23
g. 24–25
h. 33–35

Numbers 22
a. 2–6
b. 12
c. 13
d. 15–17
e. 22–27
f. 28–30
g. 31
h. 35

Numbers 23
a. 1–10
b. 11
c. 18–24

Numbers 24
a. 4–9
b. 10–11
c. 17a; Exodus 7a, b

Numbers 25
a. 4–5
b. 6–8
c. 10–13
d. 16–18

Numbers 26
a. 2, headnote
b. Headnote
c. 64–65, headnote

Numbers 27
a. 6–11
b. 12–13

c. 16–17
d. 18–21
e. 23

Numbers 28
a. 4, 9, 11, 15–19, 26,
   headnote
b. 18, 25–26

Numbers 29
a. Headnote
b. 39

Numbers 30
a. 2, headnote
b. 3–5, headnote
c. 13, headnote
d. 15

Numbers 31
a. 1–7, headnote
b. 9–18, headnote
c. 19–24
d. 49, headnote

Numbers 32
a. 1–5
b. 16–23
c. 33

Numbers 33
a. Headnote
b. 50–56

Numbers 34
a. Headnote
b. Headnote

Numbers 35
a. 1–5
b. 6, 11, 15
c. 20–25
d. 33–34

Numbers 36
a. 3–9

Deuteronomy

Introduction
   Bible Dictionary

Deuteronomy 1
a. 5

b. 7–8
c. 12–14
d. 15–17
e. 20–21
f. 22
g. 27–28
h. 29–31
i. 32–36
j. 42–43
k. 44–46

Deuteronomy 2
a. 1–7
b. 5
c. 9
d. 14
e. 19
f. 24
g. 26–29
h. 32–35

Deuteronomy 3
a. 2–3
b. 14–16
c. 23–25
d. 26–27; Numbers
    20:10–12; 12*b*
e. 28

Deuteronomy 4
a. 1, 6–8
b. 9
c. 10–14
d. D&C 84:23–24
e. 25–31
f. 32–37
g. 39–40
h. 41–42

Deuteronomy 5
a. 1
b. Exodus 20:1–17
c. 4–22
d. 24
e. 25–27
f. 29–33

Deuteronomy 6
a. 1–3
b. 5
c. 7–9
d. 10–12
e. 13, 17–18
f. 14–16

g. 20–25

Deuteronomy 7
a. 1–2, 5
b. 3–4
c. 6
d. 7–8
e. 9, 12–24
f. 25–26

Deuteronomy 8
a. 2
b. 3
c. 4*a*
d. 5
e. 7–10
f. 11–20

Deuteronomy 9
a. 1–3
b. 4
c. 4–5
d. 9–11
e. 12, 16, 23
f. 25–29

Deuteronomy 10
a. 2*b*
b. 4
c. 5
d. 8
e. 12–13

Deuteronomy 11
a. 2–7
b. 8–15, 22–25
c. 10–11
d. 16–17
e. 26–28

Deuteronomy 12
a. 2–3
b. 5–7, 10–11
c. 16, 23–24
d. 28
e. 30–31
f. 32

Deuteronomy 13
a. 1–3
b. 4
c. 5–11
d. 12–16
e. 16–17

Deuteronomy 14
a. 2
b. 6
c. 9–10
d. 22
e. 27
f. 28–29

Deuteronomy 15
a. 1–3, 4*a*
b. 4–5
c. 6
d. 7–8, 11
e. 12–15
f. 16–17

Deuteronomy 16
a. Bible Dictionary
b. Bible Dictionary
c. Bible Dictionary
d. Headnote
e. 19, 19*a*

Deuteronomy 17
a. 2–6
b. 7
c. 8–11
d. 12
e. 14–15
f. 16–17
g. 18–20

Deuteronomy 18
a. 1–4
b. 15*b*, 18*a*
c. 21–22

Deuteronomy 19
a. 4–7
b. 8–9
c. 11–12
d. 15
e. 16–19
f. 21, 21*a*

Deuteronomy 20
a. 2–4
b. 5–8
c. 10–15
d. 16–18

Deuteronomy 21
a. 1–9
b. 18–21

Deuteronomy 22
a. 1–3
b. 13–21
c. 22

Deuteronomy 23
a. 7
b. 14
c. 24

Deuteronomy 24
a. 5
b. 7
c. 14–15
d. 19–21

Deuteronomy 25
a. 5–6
b. 13–15
c. 17–19

Deuteronomy 26
a. 1–3
b. 5–10
c. 12–15
d. 16
e. 17
f. 18–19

Deuteronomy 27
a. 2–8
b. 9
c. 10
d. 14–26

Deuteronomy 28
a. 1–2
b. 3–13
c. 15
d. 16–45
e. 47–68

Deuteronomy 29
a. 1
b. 10–13
c. 18–20

Deuteronomy 30
a. 1–3
b. 4–5
c. 7
d. 11–14
e. 15–18
f. 19

Deuteronomy 31
a. 2
b. 3–6
c. 7–8
d. 10–13
e. 14–18
f. 19–21
g. 23
h. 25–30

Deuteronomy 32
a. Headnote
b. 44
c. 48–52

Deuteronomy 33
a. 1, headnote
b. 8–10, headnote
c. 13–17, headnote

Deuteronomy 34
a. 1–3
b. 4
c. Acts 7:23–29
d. Acts 7:30; Exodus 7:7
e. 7
f. 8
g. 9
h. 10–12
i. D&C 84:23
j. D&C 84:24
k. D&C 84:25

Joshua

Introduction
Bible Dictionary

Joshua 1
a. 1–9
b. 12–15
c. 16–18

Joshua 2
a. 1
b. 3–6
c. 9–11
d. 12–13
e. 14
f. 18

Joshua 3
a. 3

b. 5
c. 7–17

Joshua 4
a. 4–7, 21–24
b. 18

Joshua 5
a. 1
b. 2–7
c. 12
d. 13–15

Joshua 6
a. 11–21
b. 18
c. 22–23, 25
d. 26

Joshua 7
a. 1
b. 11–13
c. 20–21
d. 24–25

Joshua 8
a. 2
b. 9–20
c. 26
d. 29
e. 34–35

Joshua 9
a. 1–2
b. 3–14, 24
c. 15
d. 20–23

Joshua 10
a. 4
b. 6
c. 8
d. 11
e. 12–13
f. 26–27
g. 40

Joshua 11
a. 6
b. 12, 15
c. 19

Joshua 12
a. Headnote

Joshua 13
a. Headnote
b. 1

Joshua 14
a. 2
b. 4
c. 9, 13–14

Joshua 15
a. 15, 24, 29, headnote
b. 63

Joshua 16
a. Map 5
b. 10

Joshua 17
a. Headnote
b. 17–18

Joshua 18
a. 1, headnote
b. 11, headnote
c. 21–28

Joshua 19
a. 1, 10, 17, 24, 32, 40,
   headnote

Joshua 20
a. 1–3
b. 3–4
c. 6

Joshua 21
a. Headnote
b. 43–45, headnote

Joshua 22
a. 1
b. 2–6
c. 5
d. 10
e. 11–12
f. 24–28
g. 30–33

Joshua 23
a. 5
b. 6–13
c. 14
d. 15–16
e. 16

Joshua 24
a. 1–13
b. 14
c. 15
d. 16–18
e. 21–25
f. 29

Judges

Introduction
Bible Dictionary

Judges 1
a. 3
b. 6–7
c. 7
d. 12–13
e. 19
f. 28–35

Judges 2
a. 1–3
b. 4–5
c. 7
d. 10–13
e. 14–16
f. 17
g. 18, 18a
h. 19
i. 20–23

Judges 3
a. 6–7
b. 8
c. 9–10
d. 12
e. 13–14
f. 15
g. 21–22
h. 30
i. 31

Judges 4
a. 1
b. 2–4
c. 8
d. 14–15, 15a
e. 16
f. 18–21

Judges 5
a. Headnote

Judges 6
a. 1
b. 1–6
c. 11–14
d. 11, 15, 17
e. 19–21
f. 25–27
g. 30–32
h. 36–40

Judges 7
a. 2
b. 3
c. 7
d. 16–22

Judges 8
a. 5, 8
b. 6–8
c. 10
d. 10
e. 11–12
f. 18–20
g. 22–23
h. 24
i. 27
j. 30
k. 33–35

Judges 9
a. 5
b. 5
c. 21
d. 23–28
e. 43–49
f. 52–54
g. 55–57

Judges 10
a. 6
b. 7
c. 11–14
d. 15–16
e. 18

Judges 11
a. 1–3
b. 4–11
c. 12–13
d. 14–27
e. 29
f. 30–31
g. 32–33
h. 34, 39

Judges 12
a. 1
b. 6
c. 7

Judges 13
a. 1
b. 3–5
c. 8
d. 13–14
e. 19–21
f. 24

Judges 14
a. 2–4
b. 5–6
c. 8
d. 14
e. 15–18
f. 19

Judges 15
a. 2
b. 4–5
c. 6
d. 7–8
e. 15–16
f. 20

Judges 16
a. 5–6
b. 15–17
c. 21
d. 23
e. 28–30

Judges 17
a. 4
b. 5
c. 6
d. 10–13

Judges 18
a. 1
b. 2
c. 7
d. 17–20
e. 27
f. 28
g. 29
h. 30–31

Judges 19
a. 2–3

b. 3–9
c. 11–15
d. 19–21
e. 25
f. 28–30

Judges 20
a. 2
b. 4–7
c. 9–11, 11a
d. 12–13
e. 13–14
f. 18
g. 23
h. 28
i. 44–48

Judges 21
a. 2–3
b. 5
c. 8–14
d. 19–23
e. 25

Ruth

Introduction
   Bible Dictionary

Ruth 1
a. 1
b. 3–5
c. 6
d. 16–17

Ruth 2
a. 1
b. 2
c. 8–9
d. 11–12
e. 17

Ruth 3
a. 1–4
b. 11–13

Ruth 4
a. 6
b. 9–10
c. 17
d. 22

1 Samuel

Introduction
   Bible Dictionary

1 Samuel 1
a. 5–7
b. 11
c. 12–14
d. 17
e. 20
f. 28

1 Samuel 2
a. 1–10
b. 11, 11a, 18
c. 12–17, 22
d. 19
e. 21
f. 26
g. 29, 29a
h. 34
i. 35

1 Samuel 3
a. 1
b. 7
c. 8–9
d. 12–14
e. 20

1 Samuel 4
a. 2–3
b. 6–9
c. 11
d. 15
e. 18

1 Samuel 5
a. 1–2
b. 3–8
c. 9–12

1 Samuel 6
a. 7–12
b. 19

1 Samuel 7
a. 3
b. 4
c. 8
d. 13–14

1 Samuel 8
a. 1

b. 3
c. 4–5
d. 7–9
e. 11–17
f. 18
g. 19–20
h. 22

1 Samuel 9
a. 2
b. 5–6
c. 15–17
d. 21

1 Samuel 10
a. 1
b. 5–6
c. 9–11
d. 24
e. 26
f. 27

1 Samuel 11
a. 1–2
b. 6–7
c. 11
d. 15

1 Samuel 12
a. 3–5
b. 6–13
c. 14–15
d. 17
e. 21
f. 24

1 Samuel 13
a. 1–2
b. 3–4
c. 6–7
d. 8–12
e. 13–14
f. 19

1 Samuel 14
a. 1, 11–14
b. 16, 20, 20b
c. 24
d. 27
e. 45
f. 47–48
g. 52

1 Samuel 15
a. 1–3

b. 9–11, 11a
c. 11
d. 13
e. 22
f. 23
g. 23
h. 24
i. 32–33
j. 35

1 Samuel 16
a. 1
b. 7
c. 12–13
d. 13
e. 14–15, 14c
f. 15–19, 15a
g. 17–19

1 Samuel 17
a. 8–10
b. 11
c. 16
d. 17–18
e. 25
f. 26
g. 32–37
h. 40
i. 43–44
j. 45–47
k. 49–51
l. 52–53

1 Samuel 18
a. 1–4
b. 5, 14
c. 5
d. 6–9
e. 10–11
f. 12–15, 28–29
g. 20–21
h. 25
i. 30

1 Samuel 19
a. 1
b. 4–5
c. 6
d. 9–10
e. 18

1 Samuel 20
a. 5–7
b. 18–22

c. 31
d. 42

1 Samuel 21
a. 6, 9
b. 10–13

1 Samuel 22
a. 1–2
b. 3–4
c. 10, 16–19

1 Samuel 23
a. 1–4
b. 4–5
c. 10–12
d. 13
e. 16–18
f. 21–23
g. 27–28

1 Samuel 24
a. 4–6
b. 8–15
c. 16–21
d. 21–22

1 Samuel 25
a. 1
b. 3
c. 3
d. 8
e. 10–11, 14
f. 23–31
g. 32–35
h. 37–38
i. 39
j. 39–42

1 Samuel 26
a. 2
b. 8–11
c. 11–12
d. 14–16
e. 17–20, 22–24
f. 21, 25

1 Samuel 27
a. 2–3
b. 5
c. 12

1 Samuel 28
a. 1–2

b. 3
c. 4–5
d. 6–7
e. 11
f. 15
g. 17–18
h. 19

1 Samuel 29
a. 3–5
b. 6–7
c. 8
d. 9–10

1 Samuel 30
a. 1–3
b. 4
c. 7–8
d. 15
e. 17
f. 26–31

1 Samuel 31
a. 1
b. 2
c. 3–4
d. 8–13

2 Samuel 1
a. 4–10
b. 14–16
c. 17

2 Samuel 2
a. 1
b. 2–3
c. 4
d. 8–10
e. 30
f. 31

2 Samuel 3
a. 1
b. 2–5
c. 7–8
d. 12
e. 26–27, 30
f. 28–39
g. 35–37

2 Samuel 4
a. 5–7
b. 10–12

2 Samuel 5
a. 3
b. 4
c. 6–7
d. 11
e. 19
f. 20–21
g. 22–25

2 Samuel 6
a. 1–3
b. 6–7
c. 9–10
d. 11–12
e. 18
f. 20, 20a
g. 23

2 Samuel 7
a. 1–2
b. 12–13
c. 18–20
d. 29

2 Samuel 8
a. 6, 14
b. 10–11

2 Samuel 9
a. 6–7
b. 9–10

2 Samuel 10
a. 1–2
b. 3
c. 4
d. 6
e. 12
f. 17–19

2 Samuel 11
a. 1
b. 2–4
c. 5
d. 8
e. 9–11
f. 14–15
g. 16–17
h. 27
i. D&C 132:39

2 Samuel 12
a. 1
b. 5–6

c. 7–12
d. 14, 18–19
e. 24
f. 26–29

2 Samuel 13
a. 14–18
b. 19–20
c. 22
d. 28–29, 32

2 Samuel 14
a. 1
b. 19
c. 19–20
d. 21
e. 13:38; 14:28
f. 29–32
g. 33

2 Samuel 15
a. 1–6
b. 13
c. 14
d. 25–28
e. 32–37

2 Samuel 16
a. 2 Samuel 9:9–12
b. 3
c. 5–8, 13
d. 10–12
e. 15
f. 20–21
g. 23

2 Samuel 17
a. 1–3
b. 7–13
c. 15–21
d. 23
e. 25

2 Samuel 18
a. 2–3
b. 5
c. 9, 14–15
d. 33

2 Samuel 19
a. 5–7
b. 13
c. 14
d. 23

e. 29
f. 32, 39

2 Samuel 20
a. 1
b. 2
c. 3
d. 8–10
e. 16–22

2 Samuel 21
a. 1
b. 4–6
c. 9
d. 16–22

2 Samuel 22
a. 1, headnote
b. 2, headnote

2 Samuel 23
a. 2, headnote
b. 3, headnote
c. 8–38, headnote
d. 8
e. 14–18

2 Samuel 24
a. 1–2
b. 9
c. 10, headnote
d. 11–12
e. 13
f. 16, 16a
g. 17–25

1 Kings

Introduction
Bible Dictionary

1 Kings 1
a. 5–6
b. 11–21
c. 28–30
d. 33–35
e. 42–48
f. 49
g. 50–53

1 Kings 2
a. 2–4
b. 4

c. 5–9
d. 18–25
e. 26–27
f. 28–34
g. 36–46

1 Kings 3
a. 5
b. 6–9
c. 10–13
d. 14
e. 23–27

1 Kings 4
a. 21
b. 29–31
c. 34

1 Kings 5
a. 1
b. 3
c. 5
d. 6
e. 7–10
f. 12, 12b
g. 15–16

1 Kings 6
a. 7–9, 21–22
b. 11–13
c. 37–38

1 Kings 7
a. 1
b. 2, 8
c. 13–14
d. Headnote
e. 25
f. 40–46
g. 48–50
h. 51

1 Kings 8
a. 1
b. 9
c. 10–11
d. Headnote
e. 28
f. 29–49
g. 57–58
h. 61
i. 66

1 Kings 9
a. 1–2

b. 4–5
c. 6–9
d. 11
e. 12–13, 13*a*
f. 20–21
g. 22
h. 26–28

1 Kings 10
a. 1
b. 2
c. 3
d. 4–10
e. 13
f. 23

1 Kings 11
a. 4
b. 5–10
c. 11–13
d. 14–22
e. 28
f. 33, 33*c*
g. 34–38, 38*c*
h. 40

1 Kings 12
a. 1
b. 3–4
c. 6–7
d. 10–11
e. 13–16
f. 20
g. 20
h. 21–24
i. 26–33

1 Kings 13
a. 1–2
b. 3, 5
c. 4
d. 6
e. 20–30
f. 33–34

1 Kings 14
a. 1–3
b. 6–13
c. 14–16
d. 19
e. 20
f. 22–24
g. 25–26
h. 31

1 Kings 15
a. 3
b. 11–14
c. 16
d. 24
e. 25–26
f. 27–28
g. 29–30
h. 33–34

1 Kings 16
a. 1–4
b. 6, 8
c. 9–10
d. 11–12
e. 16–18
f. 21–22
g. 25–26
h. 30–33

1 Kings 17
a. 1
b. 6
c. 10–13
d. 14
e. 17–24

1 Kings 18
a. 1
b. 4
c. 17
d. 18
e. 19
f. 21
g. 36–37
h. 38
i. 39
j. 40

1 Kings 19
a. 2
b. 3–4
c. 8, 8*a*
d. 9–10
e. 12–13
f. 15–16
g. 18

1 Kings 20
a. 6, 9
b. 13–14
c. 19–21
d. 28
e. 30–34

f. 42

1 Kings 21
a. 3
b. 8–16
c. 19–24
d. 27
e. 28–29

1 Kings 22
a. 2–4
b. 5–6, 11–12
c. 17, 23–28
d. 31
e. 34–37
f. 43–46
g. 51–53

2 Kings 1
a. 3–4
b. 9–10
c. 11–12
d. 13–15
e. 16
f. 17

2 Kings 2
a. 9
b. 10
c. 11
d. 15
e. 19–22
f. 23–24, 23*a*

2 Kings 3
a. 1–3
b. 4–7
c. 11
d. 16–19
e. 27

2 Kings 4
a. 1–7
b. 8–11
c. 15–17
d. 29–36
e. 38–41

2 Kings 5
a. 1
b. 3–6
c. 8
d. 10

e. 11–12
f. 14
g. 20–24
h. 25–27

2 Kings 6
a. 8–9
b. 15–17
c. 18–20
d. 22–23
e. 23

2 Kings 7
a. 1–2
b. 6–7
c. 7–8
d. 16–20

2 Kings 8
a. 1
b. 3–6
c. 9
d. 10
e. 11–13
f. 14–15
g. 16
h. 18
i. 26–27

2 Kings 9
a. 1–3
b. 5–10
c. 22–25
d. 27–28
e. 32–37

2 Kings 10
a. 6–7
b. 11, 17
c. 18–28
d. 29
e. 35

2 Kings 11
a. 1
b. 4–8
c. 15–16
d. 17
e. 18
f. 21

2 Kings 12
a. 2
b. 5–6

c. 17–18
d. 20–21
e. 21

2 Kings 13
a. 1–2, 4
b. 3
c. 10–11
d. 13
e. 14
f. 17–19

2 Kings 14
a. 1–3
b. 5
c. 11–12
d. 13–14
e. 16
f. 17–20
g. 21
h. 29

2 Kings 15
a. 1
b. 3–4
c. 5
d. 5, 7
e. 8–9
f. 10
g. 29

2 Kings 16
a. 2–4
b. 7–9
c. 10–11
d. 17; headnote to 1
   Kings 7

2 Kings 17
a. 3–4
b. 5–6
c. 7–18
d. 18, 23
e. 24–27
f. 34–39

2 Kings 18
a. 1–4
b. 4
c. 5
d. 6
e. 28–32
f. 36

2 Kings 19
a. 2
b. 6–7
c. 10–13
d. 19
e. 20–34
f. 35
g. 36–37

2 Kings 20
a. 3
b.
c. 9–11
d. 16–18
e. 20

2 Kings 21
a. 1–7
b. 9
c. 10–16
d. 20–22
e. 23

2 Kings 22
a. 1–2
b. 3–6
c. 7
d. 8
e. 11–13
f. 14–17
g. 18–20

2 Kings 23
a. 1–2
b. 3
c. 4–20, 24
d. 20
e. 21
f. 25
g. 29–30
h. 31–32
i. 33–34
j. 37

2 Kings 24
a. 3–4
b. 9
c. 12–16
d. 17
e. 19

2 Kings 25
a. 2 Kings 24:20
b. 4–5

c. 6–7
d. 8–10
e. 21
f. 22
g. 25–26
h. 27–30

1 Chronicles

Introduction
   Bible Dictionary

1 Chronicles 1
a. 1–27, headnote
b. 28–42, headnote
c. 19

1 Chronicles 2
a. 1, 3, 13, 18, headnote

1 Chronicles 3
a. 1, headnote
b. 10–17, headnote

1 Chronicles 4
a. 1, 20, headnote
b. Headnote
c. 10

1 Chronicles 5
a. 1, Headnote
b. 24–26, headnote

1 Chronicles 6
a. 1, headnote
b. 49

1 Chronicles 7
a. 1, 6, 13, 14, 20, 30,
   headnote

1 Chronicles 8
a. 1, headnote

1 Chronicles 9
a. 1
b. 3, headnote
c. 39, headnote

1 Chronicles 10
a. 2
b. 3–4
c. 7

d. 8–10
e. 11–12
f. 13–14

1 Chronicles 11
a. 3
b. 9
c. 11
d. 17–19

1 Chronicles 12
a. 1–15, Headnote
b. 16–38, headnote
c. 38, headnote

1 Chronicles 13
a. 1–3
b. 9–10
c. 11–13
d. 14

1 Chronicles 14
a. 1–3
b. 8–12, 13–17

1 Chronicles 15
a. 2, 12–13
b. 15–16, 28
c. 29; 2 Samuel 6:20c

1 Chronicles 16
a. 2–4
b. 7
c. 8–36
d. 37

1 Chronicles 17
a. 1
b. 4–15
c. 23–27

1 Chronicles 18
a. 6
b. 11
c. 14

1 Chronicles 19
a. 2–4
b. 6–7
c. 11–13
d. 14–15
e. 17–18

1 Chronicles 20
a. 1–3

b. 5
c. 6–7

1 Chronicles 21
a. 1–8
b. 5
c. 5
d. 9–12
e. 13–14
f. 14
g. 26

1 Chronicles 22
a. 2–5, 14–15
b. 6, 11–13, 16
c. 7–10
d. 12–13
e. 17–19

1 Chronicles 23
a. 1
b. 3–5, 27–32

1 Chronicles 24
a. 1–3, 20, headnote
b. 5, 31, headnote

1 Chronicles 25
a. 1, headnote

1 Chronicles 26
a. 17–19, headnote
b. 20–32, headnote

1 Chronicles 27
a. 1, 16–22, headnote

1 Chronicles 28
a. 2–8
b. 9–10, 20–21
c. 11–19

1 Chronicles 29
a. 1–5
b. 5
c. 6–9
d. 10–19
e. 25

2 Chronicles 1
a. 7
b. 8–10
c. 11–12

2 Chronicles 2
a. 2
b. 3–10
c. 11–16

2 Chronicles 3
a. 1
b. 4–10

2 Chronicles 4
a. 2, headnote
b. 22

2 Chronicles 5
a. 4–5
b. 10
c. 13
d. 13–14

2 Chronicles 6
a. 3
b. 7–11
c. 14–42

2 Chronicles 7
a. 1–2
b. 3
c. 8
d. 11
e. 12–22
f. 19–22

2 Chronicles 8
a. 1
b. 7–8
c. 9
d. 14–15

2 Chronicles 9
a. 1
b. 2
c. 5–8
d. 9
e. 12
f. 22
g. 23
h. 29

2 Chronicles 10
a. 1
b. 3–4
c. 6–7
d. 10–11
e. 13–16

2 Chronicles 11
a. 2–4
b. 13–14
c. 14–15

2 Chronicles 12
a. 1
b. 2, 5
c. 6–8
d. 9
e. 14
f. 15

2 Chronicles 13
a. 1
b. 4–12
c. 14–15
d. 16–18

2 Chronicles 14
a. 2–7
b. 9–12
c. 13–15

2 Chronicles 15
a. 1–4
b. 8–9
c. 9
d. 12–15
e. 19

2 Chronicles 16
a. 2–5
b. 7
c. 9
d. 7, 9
e. 12

2 Chronicles 17
a. 3–6
b. 7–9
c. 9
d. 10

2 Chronicles 18
a. 1, 1a
b. 4, 6
c. 5
d. 18–22
e. 25–26
f. 31–32
g. 33–34

2 Chronicles 19
a. 2

2 Chronicles 11
a. 2–4
b. 13–14
c. 14–15

2 Chronicles 20
a. 1
b. 3
c. 12
d. 14–17
e. 22–24
f. 25
g. 33
h. 35–37

2 Chronicles 21
a. 3–4
b. 6
c. 7
d. 11
e. 12–15
f. 17–20

2 Chronicles 22
a. 1
b. 2–4
c. 7
d. 8–9
e. 10
f. 11–12

2 Chronicles 23
a. 1; 22:11
b. 1–11
c. 12–15
d. 16
e. 17
f. 18–19

2 Chronicles 24
a. 7–8
b. 12–14
c. 15
d. 16
e. 17
f. 18
g. 19–20
h. 20–22
i. 23
j. 24–25

2 Chronicles 25
a. 1–2, 2a
b. 3
c. 7–8
d. 14–15

b. 3–5
c. 6–7, 8–11

e. 15–16
f. 23–24
g. 27–28

2 Chronicles 26
a. 4–5
b. 14–15
c. 16
d. 19–21

2 Chronicles 27
a. 2
b. 6, 6a

2 Chronicles 28
a. 1–4
b. 2–5
c. 6
d. 8
e. 9–14
f. 16, 21–25

2 Chronicles 29
a. 2–3
b. 4–11
c. 15–17
d. 18–23
e. 36

2 Chronicles 30
a. 1, 5
b. 9
c. 18–20
d. 26
e. 27

2 Chronicles 31
a. 1
b. 2
c. 4–5
d. 20–21

2 Chronicles 32
a. 2–8
b. 7–8
c. 9–19
d. 20
e. 21
f. 21
g. 25
h. 26
i. 30
j. 31
k. 32; Isaiah 37–39

2 Chronicles 33
a. 1–9
b. 10
c. 11
d. 12–13
e. 22–23
f. 24
g. 25

2 Chronicles 34
a. 3, 3–7, 8
b. 14–16
c. 20–21
d. 23–28
e. 31

2 Chronicles 35
a. 3–6
b. 19
c. 21
d. 22–24

2 Chronicles 36
a. 4
b. 4
c. 5–6
d. 9–10
e. 12
f. Helaman 6:10
g. 15
h. 16–20
i. 22–23

Ezra

Introduction
    Bible Dictionary

Ezra 1
a. 1–4
b. 5
c. 6
d. 7–11

Ezra 2
a. 1
b. 62–63
c. 64–65
d. 68–69

Ezra 3
a. 2
b. 4

c. 7
d. 11–13

Ezra 4
a. 4–8
b. 11–16
c. 17–22
d. 23–24

Ezra 5
a. 1–2
b. 6–17

Ezra 6
a. 1–5
b. 6–12
c. 11
d. 13
e. 14
f. 16–18
g. 19–21

Ezra 7
a. 5
b. 6
c. 10
d. 11–26
e. 27–28

Ezra 8
a. 1
b. 21–23, 21b
c. 31

Ezra 9
a. 1–3
b. 9
c. 10–12
d. 15

Ezra 10
a. 2–4
b. 7–8
c. 10–11
d. 12–14

Nehemiah

Introduction
    Bible Dictionary

Nehemiah 1
a. 2–4

b. 8
c. 11

Nehemiah 2
a. 4–8
b. 10
c. 17–18
d. 18

Nehemiah 3
a. Headnote

Nehemiah 4
a. 7–8
b. 9
c. 14
d. 16–23

Nehemiah 5
a. 1–6
b. 10–11
c. 12
d. 14–19

Nehemiah 6
a. 2
b. 16
c. 17–19

Nehemiah 7
a. 2, headnote
b. 3
c. 7, headnote
d. 63–64, headnote
e. 65

Nehemiah 8
a. 2–3
b. 8
c. 9
d. 18

Nehemiah 9
a. 3
b. 5–30
c. 32–38

Nehemiah 10
a. 29–31, 37, headnote

Nehemiah 11
a. 1–2

Nehemiah 12
a. 1, headnote

b. 27, headnote
c. 44–45, headnote

Nehemiah 13
a. 1–3
b. 4–5
c. 7–13
d. 15–21
e. 23–30

Esther

Introduction
  Bible Dictionary

Esther 1
a. 1
b. 10–11
c. 12, 17–20

Esther 2
a. 2–4
b. 5–7
c. 9
d. 17
e. 21–23

Esther 3
a. 1–5
b. 9–11

Esther 4
a. 7–9, 13–14
b. 11
c. 15–16

Esther 5
a. 1–2
b. 4
c. 14

Esther 6
a. 1–3
b. 4
c. 10

Esther 7
a. 3–4, 6
b. 9–10

Esther 8
a. 2
b. 5–6

c. 7–8
d. 11

Esther 9
a. 2–4
b. 10, 13–14
c. 16
d. 20–23
e. 24–26, headnote

Esther 10
a. 2–3

Job

Introduction
  Bible Dictionary

Job 1
a. 1–5
b. 7
c. 11
d. 12
e. 13–19
f. 20–22

Job 2
a. 5
b. 6
c. 7
d. 9
e. 10
f. 11–13

Job 3
a. 1–3, headnote
b. 11, headnote

Job 4
a. 7–9, 17, headnote

Job 5
a. 17–18, headnote

Job 6
a. 8–9
b. 24–25

Job 7
a. 1, 17, 21, headnote

Job 8
a. 3, headnote

Job 9
a. 1–4, headnote

Job 10
a. 7
b. 8–9

Job 11
a. 1–5
b. 13–14

Job 12
a. 10, 12–25, headnote

Job 13
a. 15, headnote

Job 14
a. 14, headnote
b. 14, headnote

Job 15
a. 16–25, headnote

Job 16
a. 16–22

Job 17
a. 10–16, headnote

Job 18
a. 5–21, headnote

Job 19
a. 25–27

Job 20
a. 4–8

Job 21
a. 7–14, headnote
b. 30–33, headnote

Job 22
a. 5–7, headnote
b. 21–23, 27–28, headnote

Job 23
a. 1–7, headnote
b. 10–12

Job 24
a. 24, headnote

Job 25
a. 1–6, headnote

Job 26
a. 1–7, headnote

Job 27
a. 13–23, headnote

Job 28
a. 1–2, 5, headnote
b. 12–19, headnote
c. 28

Job 29
a. Headnote
b. 12–16

Job 30
a. 1, headnote
b. 25

Job 31
a. 35, headnote

Job 32
a. 7–9, headnote

Job 33
a. 12–15, 24, headnote

Job 34
a. 12, headnote

Job 35
a. 8, headnote

Job 36
a. 5–11, headnote
b. 12–14, headnote

Job 37
a. 2–5, headnote
b. 21–22, headnote

Job 38
a. 1–7, headnote
b. Headnote

Job 39
a. Headnote

Job 40
a. 3–5, headnote

b. 6–14, headnote

Job 41
a. 11, headnote
b. Bible Dictionary

Job 42
a. 5
b. 6
c. 7–8
d. 10–15

Psalms

Introduction
  Bible Dictionary

Psalm 1
a. 1–2
b. 3
c. 4–6

Psalm 2
a. 10–12

Psalm 3
a. 3–5

Psalm 4
a. 1

Psalm 5
a. 11

Psalm 6
a. 2–7

Psalm 7
a. 1

Psalm 8
a. 4
b. 5, 5*a*
c. 6–8

Psalm 9
a. Headnote

Psalm 10
a. 2–11

Psalm 11
a. 5–7

Psalm 12
a. 1–5

Psalm 13
a. 5, headnote

Psalm 14
a. 1

Psalm 15
a. 1
b. 2–5

Psalm 16
a. 11

Psalm 17
a. 1–13, headnote

Psalm 18
a. Headnote

Psalm 19
a. 1, 7, 9, headnote

Psalm 20
a. 6

Psalm 21
a. Headnote

Psalm 22
a. Headnote
b. Headnote
c. 27–28

Psalm 23
a. 1
b. 2–5
c. 6

Psalm 24
a. 1–2
b. 3–5

Psalm 25
a. 10

Psalm 26
a. 1, 8, headnote

Psalm 27
a. 1
b. 4

c. 14

Psalm 28
a. 9, headnote

Psalm 29
a. 2, headnote

Psalm 30
a. 1–12, headnote

Psalm 31
a. 23–24

Psalm 32
a. 1–2

Psalm 33
a. 12

Psalm 34
a. 8–22

Psalm 35
a. 11–21

Psalm 36
a. 5, headnote

Psalm 37
a. 1–2
b. 3–11
c. 39–40

Psalm 38
a. 12, 19–20

Psalm 39
a. 1–3, headnote

Psalm 40
a. Headnote

Psalm 41
a. 1–3

Psalm 42
a. Headnote

Psalm 43
a. 3

Psalm 44
a. 1–8, headnote

Psalm 45
a. 17, headnote

Psalm 46
a. 1–11, headnote

Psalm 47
a. 7–9

Psalm 48
a. 1–3, 14, headnote

Psalm 49
a. 16–17, headnote

Psalm 50
a. 5

Psalm 51
a. 1–14, headnote
b. 17

Psalm 52
a. 1–3, headnote

Psalm 53
a. 1

Psalm 54
a. 1, headnote

Psalm 55
a. 16–23, headnote

Psalm 56
a. 1–3, headnote

Psalm 57
a. 5, 9–11, headnote

Psalm 58
a. 1–5, headnote

Psalm 59
a. 1–2

Psalm 60
a. 7, headnote

Psalm 61
a. 1–4, headnote

Psalm 62
a. 12

Psalm 63
a. 1, headnote

Psalm 64
a. 10

Psalm 65
a. 4, headnote

Psalm 66
a. 10

Psalm 67
a. 4

Psalm 68
a. 35

Psalm 69
a. 35

Psalm 70
a. 4, headnote

Psalm 71
a. Headnote

Psalm 72
a. 1–5, 12–14

Psalm 73
a. 24, headnote

Psalm 74
a. 3–9

Psalm 75
a. 1, headnote

Psalm 76
a. 8–9, headnote

Psalm 77
a. 1–3, headnote

Psalm 78
a. 4–8, headnote

Psalm 79
a. 8–10, headnote

Psalm 80
a. 1–7, headnote

Psalm 81
a. 13–16, headnote

Psalm 82
a. 6

Psalm 83
a. 18, headnote

Psalm 84
a. 11

Psalm 85
a. 11, headnote

Psalm 86
a. 9, headnote

Psalm 87
a. 5, headnote

Psalm 88
a. Headnote

Psalm 89
a. Headnote

Psalm 90
a. 12–17, headnote

Psalm 91
a. 15, headnote

Psalm 92
a. 1–2

Psalm 93
a. 5

Psalm 94
a. 12–15, headnote

Psalm 95
a. 8–11, headnote

Psalm 96
a. 13

Psalm 97
a. 10

Psalm 98
a. 1–9, headnote

Psalm 99
a. 2

Psalm 100
a. 2
b. 3–5

Psalm 101
a. 1, headnote

Psalm 102
a. 16

Psalm 103
a. 17–18, headnote

Psalm 104
a. 1

Psalm 105
a. 13–15

Psalm 106
a. 34–43, headnote

Psalm 107
a. 8

Psalm 108
a. 8, headnote

Psalm 109
a. 1–20, headnote

Psalm 110
a. 4, headnote

Psalm 111
a. 2–10

Psalm 112
a. 1–9

Psalm 113
a. 1–9

Psalm 114
a. Headnote

Psalm 115
a. 4–8, headnote

Psalm 116
a. 15

Psalm 117
a. 1–2

Psalm 118
a. 1–4

Psalm 119
a. 1–3
b. 10–16
c. 24
d. 30–32
e. 33–40
f. 46
g. 49–52
h. 63
i. 66–68
j. 73
k. 84–87
l. 92
m. 104
n. 105
o. 116–17
p. 127
q. 133
r. 144
s. 150
t. 153–56
u. 165
v. 169–76

Psalm 120
a. 1

Psalm 121
a. 1–2, 7–8

Psalm 122
a. Headnote

Psalm 123
a. 3

Psalm 124
a. 8

Psalm 125
a. Headnote

Psalm 126
a. 2–3, headnote

Psalm 127
a. 1
b. 3–5

c. 3–5

Psalm 128
a. 1

Psalm 129
a. 5–8

Psalm 130
a. 1–8, headnote

Psalm 131
a. 3

Psalm 132
a. 11

Psalm 133
a. 1

Psalm 134
a. 1–2

Psalm 135
a. 5–12
b. 15–18

Psalm 136
a. 1, 26

Psalm 137
a. 1

Psalm 138
a. 1–3, 7–8, headnote

Psalm 139
a. 7, 21, headnote

Psalm 140
a. 1–11
b. 12

Psalm 141
a. 1–10, headnote

Psalm 142
a. 5–7, headnote

Psalm 143
a. 5, headnote

Psalm 144
a. 15, headnote

Psalm 145
a. 18
b. 19–20

Psalm 146
a. 7–9

Psalm 147
a. 1–6
b. 10–11

Psalm 148
a. 1–13, headnote

Psalm 149
a. 4

Psalm 150
a. 1–5
b. 6

Proverbs

Introduction
  Bible Dictionary

Proverbs 1
a. 7
b. 7
c. 8
d. 10–15
e. 33

Proverbs 2
a. 1–5
b. 14a
c. 20
d. 21

Proverbs 3
a. 5–7
b. 9–10
c. 12
d. 13–15
e. 35

Proverbs 4
a. 5–9
b. 18
c. 19

Proverbs 5
a. 21

b. 22

Proverbs 6
a. 16–19
b. 32–33

Proverbs 7
a. 24–27, headnote
b. Headnote

Proverbs 8
a. 11, headnote
b. 22–31, headnote

Proverbs 9
a. 6–8
b. 8
c. 9
d. 13–18

Proverbs 10
a. 1
b. 13
c. 14

Proverbs 11
a. 12
b. 14
c. 16
d. 22
e. 29

Proverbs 12
a. 1
b. 4
c. 10
d. 15
e. 22

Proverbs 13
a. 1
b. 10
c. 18
d. 20
e. 24

Proverbs 14
a. 5
b. 15
c. 15
d. 21
e. 23
f. 34
g. 35

Proverbs 15
a. 1
b. 1
c. 12
d. 22
e. 26
f. 33

Proverbs 16
a. 5
b. 16
c. 18
d. 20
e. 29–30
f. 31a
g. 32

Proverbs 17
a. 6
b. 6
c. 13
d. 15
e. 27
f. 28

Proverbs 18
a. 9
b. 13
c. 19
d. 22
e. 24

Proverbs 19
a. 1–2
b. 14
c. 17
d. 20

Proverbs 20
a. 1
b. 29

Proverbs 21
a. 3
b. 10
c. 13
d. 17
e. 20
f. 31

Proverbs 22
a. 1
b. 6
c. 15

d. 16, 22–23

Proverbs 23
a. 6–7
b. 9
c. 17
d. 20–21
e. 22

Proverbs 24
a. 6
b. 8
c. 19–20

Proverbs 25
a. 6–7
b. 19
c. 21–22
d. 28

Proverbs 26
a. 4
b. 20
c. 27

Proverbs 27
a. 12
b. 20a

Proverbs 28
a. 1
b. 5
c. 13
d. 26
e. 27

Proverbs 29
a. 2
b. 2
c. 7
d. 18
e. 23

Proverbs 30
a. 1
b. 7–8
c. 18–19

Proverbs 31
a. 1
b. 3–5
c. 9
d. 10
e. 30

Ecclesiastes

Introduction
 Bible Dictionary

Ecclesiastes 1
a. 1
b. 2b
c. 13
d. 18

Ecclesiastes 2
a. 9–11, 17, headnote
b. 26

Ecclesiastes 3
a. 1
b. 17

Ecclesiastes 4
a. 1–4
b. 13

Ecclesiastes 5
a. 2–3
b. 19

Ecclesiastes 6
a. 3, headnote

Ecclesiastes 7
a. 11–12, 19

Ecclesiastes 8
a. 8, headnote
b. Headnote

Ecclesiastes 9
a. 1
b. 16
c. 18

Ecclesiastes 10
a. 1, headnote
b. 12
c. 14

Ecclesiastes 11
a. 6, headnote
b. 9, headnote

Ecclesiastes 12
a. 7
b. 11

c. 13

The Song of Solomon

Introduction
 Bible Dictionary

Isaiah

Introduction
 Bible Dictionary

Isaiah 1
a. 2–4, headnote
b. 9, headnote
c. 16–19, headnote
d. 27, headnote

Isaiah 2
a. 1–4, headnote
b. 12–21, headnote

Isaiah 3
a. 5–8, headnote
b. 13, headnote
c. 16–21, headnote

Isaiah 4
a. 1, 4, headnote

Isaiah 5
a. 7, headnote
b. 45, 24–25, headnote

Isaiah 6
a. 1, headnote
b. 7, headnote
c. 9–10, headnote
d. 6a

Isaiah 7
a. 1, 5–6, headnote
b. 9b

Isaiah 8
a. 14, headnote
b. 19, headnote
c. 16, 20, headnote

Isaiah 9
a. 2, headnote
b. 6–7, headnote

c. 18–19, headnote

Isaiah 10
a. 5–6, headnote
b. 19–20, headnote
c. 21–22, headnote

Isaiah 11
a. 1, headnote
b. 3–4, headnote
c. 9, headnote
d. 10–12, headnote

Isaiah 12
a. 4–6, headnote
b. 6, headnote

Isaiah 13
a. 9, 11, headnote
b. 6, 9, 13, headnote
c. 19, headnote

Isaiah 14
a. 1–3, 7, headnote
b. 13–14, headnote
c. 22–23, headnote

Isaiah 15
a. 1, headnote
b. 2–5, headnote

Isaiah 16
a. 5, headnote

Isaiah 17
a. 10, headnote
b. 12–14, headnote

Isaiah 18
a. 3, headnote

Isaiah 19
a. 22, headnote
b. 23–25, headnote

Isaiah 20
a. 4, headnote

Isaiah 21
a. 9, headnote

Isaiah 22
a. 1–2, 5–9, headnote
b. 3, headnote

c. 20–24, headnote

Isaiah 23
a. 1, headnote

Isaiah 24
a. 5, headnote
b. 6, 20, 23, headnote
c. 23, headnote

Isaiah 25
a. 6, headnote
b. 9, headnote

Isaiah 26
a. 3–4, headnote
b. 19, headnote
c. 19, headnote

Isaiah 27
a. 6, 12–13, headnote

Isaiah 28
a. 5a
b. 16, headnote

Isaiah 29
a. 4, headnote
b. 10–14, headnote

Isaiah 30
a. 10–11, headnote
b. 23–26, 29, headnote
c. 27–28, 30, headnote

Isaiah 31
a. 1, headnote
b. 4–5, headnote

Isaiah 32
a. 1, headnote
b. 13–20, headnote

Isaiah 33
a. 1, 11, 14, headnote
b. 10–14, headnote
c. 20, 24, headnote
d. 22, headnote

Isaiah 34
a. 1–2, 8, headnote
b. 2, headnote
c. 5, headnote

Isaiah 35
a. 1–4, 8–10, headnote

Isaiah 36
a. 1, 18–20, headnote

Isaiah 37
a. 1–5, 14–20, headnote
b. 6–7, 31–34, headnote
c. 36, headnote
d. 38, headnote

Isaiah 38
a. 7–8, headnote
b. 19–20, headnote

Isaiah 39
a. 1–2, headnote
b. 5–7, headnote

Isaiah 40
a. 3–4, headnote
b. 13–18, 25–26, headnote

Isaiah 41
a. 8–9, headnote
b. 23–24, headnote

Isaiah 42
a. 3–7, headnote

Isaiah 43
a. 3, 5–6, 11–13, headnote

Isaiah 44
a. 3, headnote
b. 22–23, 26–28, headnote

Isaiah 45
a. 13, headnote
b. 23, headnote

Isaiah 46
a. 1–5, headnote
b. 9, 13, headnote

Isaiah 47
a. 10–11, headnote

Isaiah 48
a. 6–8, headnote

b. 10, headnote

Isaiah 49
a. 9, headnote
b. 5–6, headnote
c. 22–23, headnote

Isaiah 50
a. 4–7, headnote

Isaiah 51
a. 3, 11, headnote
b. 10–11, headnote

Isaiah 52
a. 8, headnote
b. 9

Isaiah 53
a. 3–5, headnote
b. 10, headnote
c. 12, headnote

Isaiah 54
a. 2–3, headnote
b. 7–8, headnote

Isaiah 55
a. 3, headnote
b. 6, headnote

Isaiah 56
a. 1–5, headnote
b. 6–8, headnote

Isaiah 57
a. 1–2, headnote
b. 15, headnote
c. 21, headnote

Isaiah 58
a. 6–7
b. 8–12
c. 13–14

Isaiah 59
a. 2, headnote
b. 12–13, headnote
c. 16–20, headnote

Isaiah 60
a. Headnote
b. 3, 10–12, headnote
c. 14–15

d. 17–20

Isaiah 61
a. 1, headnote
b. 6–9, headnote

Isaiah 62
a. 6, headnote
b. 7, headnote

Isaiah 63
a. 4, headnote
b. 16, headnote

Isaiah 64
a. 1–4, headnote

Isaiah 65
a. 1–2, headnote
b. 17–18, headnote

Isaiah 66
a. 8, 15–16, 19, headnote

Jeremiah

Introduction
Bible Dictionary

Jeremiah 1
a. 5, headnote
b. 9–10, 17, headnote

Jeremiah 2
a. 13, 27, 30, headnote

Jeremiah 3
a. 2, headnote
b. 14–19, headnote

Jeremiah 4
a. 1–4, headnote
b. 11–27, headnote

Jeremiah 5
a. 1–11, headnote
b. 24–25, headnote

Jeremiah 6
a. 1, 19, headnote

Jeremiah 7
a. 3, 5–7, headnote

b. 11, headnote
c. 24–26, 31, headnote

Jeremiah 8
a. 10–13, headnote

Jeremiah 9
a. 16, headnote

Jeremiah 10
a. 10–11, headnote

Jeremiah 11
a. 2–4, headnote
b. 11, headnote

Jeremiah 12
a. 1–4, headnote
b. 16, headnote

Jeremiah 13
a. 7–10, headnote
b. 19, headnote

Jeremiah 14
a. 1–4, headnote
b. 10, 14, headnote

Jeremiah 15
a. 2, headnote
b. 4, headnote

Jeremiah 16
a. 9–13, headnote
b. 16, headnote
c. 19–21, headnote

Jeremiah 17
a. 13, headnote
b. 21–25, headnote

Jeremiah 18
a. 6, headnote
b. 10–11, headnote
c. 17, headnote

Jeremiah 19
a. 3–4, headnote
b. 9, headnote

Jeremiah 20
a. 2, headnote
b. 4–6, headnote

Jeremiah 21
a. 4–7, headnote
b. 7, headnote

Jeremiah 22
a. 1–5, headnote
b. 24–30, headnote

Jeremiah 23
a. 3, headnote
b. 5–6, headnote
c. 30–32, headnote

Jeremiah 24
a. 8–10, headnote
b. 5–6, headnote

Jeremiah 25
a. 11, headnote
b. 15–16, 31–33, headnote

Jeremiah 26
a. 4–6, headnote
b. 8, 24, headnote

Jeremiah 27
a. 8, headnote

Jeremiah 28
a. 1–4, headnote

Jeremiah 29
a. 4–10, headnote
b. 18, headnote
c. 31, headnote

Jeremiah 30
a. 3, headnote
b. 9, headnote

Jeremiah 31
a. 9, headnote
b. 31, headnote

Jeremiah 32
a. 2, headnote
b. 37–44, headnote

Jeremiah 33
a. 7, headnote
b. 17, 21–22, headnote

Jeremiah 34
a. 2–5, headnote

b. 17, headnote

Jeremiah 35
a. 18, headnote
b. 19

Jeremiah 36
a. 4, headnote
b. 21–23, headnote
c. 27–32, headnote

Jeremiah 37
a. 7–8, headnote
b. 21, headnote

Jeremiah 38
a. 6, headnote
b. 17–21, headnote

Jeremiah 39
a. 1–9, headnote
b. 10, headnote

Jeremiah 40
a. 5, headnote
b. 1, 4, headnote

Jeremiah 41
a. 2, headnote

Jeremiah 42
a. 10–12, headnote
b. 15–16, headnote

Jeremiah 43
a. 4–6, headnote
b. 10–13, headnote

Jeremiah 44
a. 12, 15–17, headnote

Jeremiah 45
a. 5, headnote

Jeremiah 46
a. 13, headnote
b. 27–28, headnote

Jeremiah 47
a. 4, headnote

Jeremiah 48
a. 2, 4, 42, headnote

Jeremiah 49
a. Headnote

Jeremiah 50
a. 3, headnote
b. 19, headnote

Jeremiah 51
a. 1–6, headnote
b. 45, headnote

Jeremiah 52
a. 5–7, headnote
b. 13–14, 17–30, headnote

Lamentations

Introduction
Bible Dictionary

Lamentations 1
a. 1–11, headnote
b. 12–22, headnote

Lamentations 2
a. 1–22, headnote

Lamentations 3
a. 55–66, headnote

Lamentations 4
a. 13, headnote

Lamentations 5
a. 1–22, headnote

Ezekiel

Introduction
Bible Dictionary

Ezekiel 1
a. 5, 5–16, 26–27, headnote

Ezekiel 2
a. 3, 7, headnote
b. 10, headnote

Ezekiel 3
a. 17, headnote
b. 18, headnote

Ezekiel 4
a. 1–3, headnote

Ezekiel 5
a. 12, headnote

Ezekiel 6
a. 2–4, headnote
b. 8, headnote

Ezekiel 7
a. 15, 25, headnote

Ezekiel 8
a. 6, 16, headnote

Ezekiel 9
a. 2–6, headnote

Ezekiel 10
a. 1–5, 9, headnote

Ezekiel 11
a. 5–16, headnote
b. 17–20, headnote

Ezekiel 12
a. 14–15, headnote

Ezekiel 13
a. 2, 6, 10, headnote

Ezekiel 14
a. 4, headnote
b. 6, headnote

Ezekiel 15
a. 6, headnote

Ezekiel 16
a. 15, headnote
b. 17–26, headnote
c. 60–63, headnote

Ezekiel 17
a. 12–17, headnote

Ezekiel 18
a. 4, headnote
b. 14–17, headnote
c. 20, headnote
d. 21, headnote

Ezekiel 19
a. 4, 8, headnote

Ezekiel 20
a. 5–29, headnote

b. 34–38, 41–42, headnote

Ezekiel 21
a. 3–4, headnote
b. 19–32, headnote

Ezekiel 22
a. 2–13, headnote
b. 15–31, headnote

Ezekiel 23
a. 4, headnote
b. 5–8, 11–21, headnote
c. 9–10, 23–25, headnote

Ezekiel 24
a. 1–4, headnote
b. 15–24, headnote

Ezekiel 25
a. 2–7, 8–11, 13, 15–17, headnote

Ezekiel 26
a. 2, headnote

Ezekiel 27
a. Headnote

Ezekiel 28
a. 12–16, 21–24, headnote
b. 25–26, headnote

Ezekiel 29
a. 19, headnote
b. 13–14, headnote

Ezekiel 30
a. 6–7, headnote

Ezekiel 31
a. 2, headnote

Ezekiel 32
a. 2, headnote

Ezekiel 33
a. 2–5, headnote
b. 14–16, headnote
c. 13, 18, headnote
d. 23–29, headnote

Ezekiel 34
a. 2–3, headnote
b. 12, 23, 25, headnote

Ezekiel 35
a. 3, 5, headnote

Ezekiel 36
a. 24, headnote
b. 26, headnote

Ezekiel 37
a. 12–13, headnote
b. 16–17, headnote
c. 21, headnote
d. 24–27, headnote

Ezekiel 38
a. Headnote
b. 9–16, 21, headnote
c. 19–20, headnote

Ezekiel 39
a. 1–5, headnote
b. 9, headnote
c. 12, headnote
d. 17, 21–29, headnote

Ezekiel 40
a. Headnote

Ezekiel 41
a. Headnote

Ezekiel 42
a. Headnote

Ezekiel 43
a. 4–5, headnote
b. 7, headnote
c. 7, headnote

Ezekiel 44
a. 4, headnote
b. 9, headnote
c. 10–11, 14–23, 27, headnote

Ezekiel 45
a. 4, headnote
b. 6–16, headnote

Ezekiel 46
a. Headnote

Ezekiel 47
a. 1–9, headnote
b. 13–21, headnote

Ezekiel 48
a. 31, headnote
b. 35, headnote

Daniel

Introduction
Bible Dictionary

Daniel 1
a. 3–4
b. 12, 12a
c. 15, 17
d. 18–20

Daniel 2
a. 1
b. 17–19
c. 27
d. 28
e. 34–35, headnote;
D&C 65:2
f. 46–49

Daniel 3
a. 1–3
b. 6
c. 8–13
d. 16–18
e. 20–22
f. 25
g. 27
h. 29

Daniel 4
a. 6–8
b. 10–18
c. 17
d. 20–26
e. 27
f. 30–32
g. 33
h. 34–36
i. 37

Daniel 5
a. 1–4
b. 5–6
c. 10–11

d. 16
e. 17
f. 18–21
g. 22–23
h. 26–28
i. 30
j. 31

Daniel 6
a. 1–2
b. 3
c. 4–5
d. 10
e. 13–14
f. 16
g. 18
h. 22–23
i. 26–27

Daniel 7
a. 3–8
b. 9c
c. 9–14
d. 17, headnote
e. 18
f. 21
g. 23–25
h. 26–27

Daniel 8
a. 20–21, headnote
b. 23–24, headnote
c. 25, headnote

Daniel 9
a. 3, headnote
b. 21–27

Daniel 10
a. Headnote
b. 5–6
c. 7

Daniel 11
a. Headnote

Daniel 12
a. 1
b. 2–3
c. 10

Hosea

Introduction
Bible Dictionary

Hosea 1
a. 4, 6, 9, headnote
b. 10, headnote

Hosea 2
a. 1–13, headnote
b. 18–23, headnote

Hosea 3
a. 1–5, headnote

Hosea 4
a. 1, headnote

Hosea 5
a. 5, headnote

Hosea 6
a. 1, headnote
b. 6, headnote

Hosea 7
a. 1–4, headnote
b. 8, headnote

Hosea 8
a. 14, headnote
b. 12, headnote

Hosea 9
a. Headnote
b. Headnote

Hosea 10
a. 1–4, 13, headnote
b. 12, headnote

Hosea 11
a. 1, headnote
b. 3–5, headnote

Hosea 12
a. 10, headnote
b. 14, headnote
c. 14, headnote

Hosea 13
a. 1–2, headnote
b. 14, headnote

Hosea 14
a. 7–8, headnote

Joel

Introduction
Bible Dictionary

Joel 1
a. 14, headnote

Joel 2
a. 2–8, 10, 28, headnote

Joel 3
a. 9–11, headnote
b. 12–14, headnote
c. 16–17, headnote

Amos

Introduction
Bible Dictionary

Amos 1
a. Headnote

Amos 2
a. Headnote

Amos 3
a. 7, headnote
b. 9–11, headnote

Amos 4
a. 6–7, headnote
b. 8, headnote

Amos 5
a. 4, headnote
b. Headnote

Amos 6
a. 7, headnote

Amos 7
a. 16–17, headnote

Amos 8
a. 11–12, headnote

Amos 9
a. 9, headnote
b. 13–15, headnote

Obadiah

Introduction
Bible Dictionary

Obadiah 1
a. 1–9, headnote
b. 21, 21a, headnote

Jonah

Introduction
Bible Dictionary

Jonah 1
a. 2, headnote
b. 17, headnote

Jonah 2
a. 10, headnote

Jonah 3
a. 4, headnote
b. 5, headnote

Jonah 4
a. 1–2, headnote
b. 4–11, headnote

Micah

Introduction
Bible Dictionary

Micah 1
a. 1–9, headnote

Micah 2
a. 1–4, headnote
b. 12, headnote

Micah 3
a. Headnote

Micah 4
a. Headnote

Micah 5
a. 2, headnote
b. 7–8, headnote

Micah 6
a. 1–7, headnote

b. 8, headnote

Micah 7
a. 18–20, headnote

Nahum

Introduction
 Bible Dictionary

Nahum 1
a. Headnote

Nahum 2
a. Headnote
b. Headnote

Nahum 3
a. Headnote

Habakkuk

Introduction
 Bible Dictionary

Habakkuk 1
a. 1–10, headnote

Habakkuk 2
a. 4, headnote
b. 14, headnote

Habakkuk 3
a. Headnote

Zephaniah

Introduction
 Bible Dictionary

Zephaniah 1
a. Headnote
b. 15–16, headnote

Zephaniah 2
a. 3, headnote

Zephaniah 3
a. 1–8
b. 9
c. 17

Haggai

Introduction
 Bible Dictionary

Haggai 1
a. 4–11, headnote

Haggai 2
a. 9, headnote

Zechariah

Introduction
 Bible Dictionary

Zechariah 1
a. 2–6, headnote
b. 12–17, headnote

Zechariah 2
a. 1–4, headnote
b. 6, headnote
c. 10, headnote

Zechariah 3
a. 9, headnote

Zechariah 4
a. 9, headnote

Zechariah 5
a. Headnote

Zechariah 6
a. 11, headnote
b. 13, headnote

Zechariah 7
a. Headnote
b. 9–10, headnote

Zechariah 8
a. Headnote

Zechariah 9
a. 11–12, headnote

Zechariah 10
a. 1–5, headnote
b. 6–8, 12, headnote

Zechariah 11
a. 12, headnote

b. 13, headnote

Zechariah 12
a. 2, headnote
b. 3, headnote
c. 10, headnote

Zechariah 13
a. 1–2, headnote
b. 6
c. 9

Zechariah 14
a. 1–2, headnote
b. 3, headnote
c. 9, headnote
d. 12, headnote

Malachi

Introduction
 Bible Dictionary

Malachi 1
a. 6–7, headnote
b. 14, headnote

Malachi 2
a. 8, headnote
b. 10–16, headnote

Malachi 3
a. 1, headnote
b. 10, headnote
c. 16, headnote

Malachi 4
a. 1, headnote
b. 5; D&C 110:13–16

Moses

Introduction
 Bible Dictionary

Moses 1
a. 1
b. 2, 11
c. 4–5
d. 7–8
e. 12
f. 13–18

g. 19–22
h. 24–29
i. 33
j. 39
k. 41–42

Moses 2
a. 2:2–31, 3:2–4

Moses 3
a. 3
b. 5
c. 7
d. 8
e. 9
f. Bible Dictionary
g. 17
h. 19–20
i. 24

Moses 4
a. 1
b. 2
c. 3
d. 4
e. 6
f. 13
g. 22
h. 23–25
i. 28

Moses 5
a. 4
b. 5
c. 6
d. 7–8
e. 9–11
f. 13
g. 14
h. 18
i. 5, 19–21
j. 26
k. 28
l. 29–31
m. 33
n. 36–41
o. 49–50
p. 53–54
q. 58

Moses 6
a. 3
b. 5, 46
c. 5

d. 12
e. 15
f. 22–23
g. 26–30
h. 31
i. 32–34
j. 35–36
k. 37–39
l. 50
m. 51–52
n. 55–62
o. 60
p. 64–66

Moses 7
a. 1
b. 3–4
c. 3–4
d. 7–8
e. 13
f. 18
g. 19
h. 25–27
i. 27
j. 32–34, 37
k. 33–36
l. 41–44
m. 47
n. 48

o. 50–52
p. 54–64
q. 62
r. 62–63
s. 65–66
t. 69

Moses 8
a. 2
b. 4
c. 7
d. 13
e. 18
f. 19
g. 22
h. 23–24
i. 27
j. 28–30

Abraham

Introduction
a. Bible Dictionary
b. Bible Dictionary
c. Bible Dictionary
d. Bible Dictionary
e. Bible Dictionary
f. D&C 132:29, 37

g. Bible Dictionary
h. Bible Dictionary
i. Bible Dictionary
j. Bible Dictionary
k. Bible Dictionary
l. Bible Dictionary
m. Bible Dictionary
n. Bible Dictionary

Abraham 1
a. Headnote
b. 2, headnote
c. 5–7
d. 15–19
e. 19
f. 20
g. 25
h. 25
i. 26
j. 26
k. 26–27
l. 29–30
m. 31

Abraham 2
a. 3
b. 4
c. 6–11
d. 12–13

e. 17
f. 19
g. 21
h. 22–24

Abraham 3
a. 1
b. 3
c. 4
d. 11
e. 11
f. 14
g. 17
h. 19
i. 22
j. 23
k. 24–25
l. 26
m. 27–28

Abraham 4
a. 4:1–31; 5:1–3

Abraham 5
a. 9
b. 11
c. 13; 3:4
d. 14
e. 20–21